Living to be a Hundred

Ivor Felstein

Living to be a Hundred

A STUDY OF OLD AGE

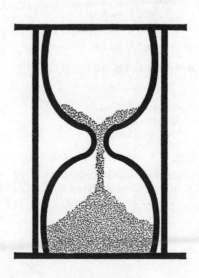

HIPPOCRENE
BOOKS, INC.

Hippocrene Books, Inc.
171 Madison Avenue
New York, N.Y. 10016

First published in Great Britain in 1973 by

David & Charles
South Devon House
Newton Abbot, Devon

First published in the United States 1973
Library of Congress Catalog Number 73-83141
ISBN 0-88254-172-2

Printed in Great Britain

FOR SHIRLEY AND BARRY FREEMAN

Contents

Introduction: A Human Elite

IN 1969, THE STAY YOUNG RESEARCH CORPORATION WAS OCCUPY-
ing offices in the home of American advertising, Madison
Avenue, New York. Among its many activities this organisation was publishing each month a bright and sunny pamphlet
entitled *Stay Young Newsletter,* which contained short interesting items under such eye-catching headings as 'Medical
reports that could affect your life', 'New foods' and 'Beware
these practices'. The most intriguing heading in one edition
was the matter-of-fact statement 'How to live to be 100', intro-
ducing a piece quoted from a study by J. Szafran on middle-
aged aircraft pilots. The eyesight, hearing and learning
capacity of these middle-aged pilots had been measured carefully and the results compared with those of aircraft pilots in
their twenties. All in good health, the middle-aged pilots were
not suffering from any significant or serious complaint. In
terms of the findings in that study, Dr Szafran was quoted as
saying, age could not be equated directly with decline and age
alone should not be considered sufficient reason for retirement. Many healthy business executives, shop floor workers
and senior professional employees in different countries
throughout the world, unwillingly but compulsorily retired
solely on grounds of age, would echo that conclusion.

The Szafran study impresses on us the fact that human
faculties do not, as a general rule, wear out by middle age.
The results also indicate that the process of 'wearing out'
varies from one individual to another. A New York physician,
F. Yandel, who was quoted in the same article, stated that
healthy older people (presumably by contrast with sick older

people) invariably display a 'sense of humour' which shows up strongly in personal and sexual matters. From this, the editor of the newsletter rightly concluded that lack of joie de vivre is often a prelude to lack of life itself. Although neither the Szafran study nor the Yandel statement gave any definite information on *how* to live to be 100, that title was not altogether misleading for, as we shall confirm in later chapters, occupation and attitude of mind do indeed influence individual length of life.

There is an early morning radio programme transmitted by the British Broadcasting Corporation which includes, among various musical request sections, birthday congratulations for United Kingdom senior citizens. Unwittingly perhaps, this particular practice emphasises the rising number of people in the United Kingdom who are reaching birthdays in the eighth, ninth and tenth decades of life. At present a figure of 115 years of age (some gerontologists argue a figure of 120 years) is taken as the real or physiological upper limit an individual life can aspire to. This means that 100, 90 and even 80 years of age is not only a great chronological prize but a significant landmark in human longevity. If this is so in Britain, Europe, North America, Australia and New Zealand—which it certainly is—it represents an even greater achievement in longevity in emerging and developing countries such as those of North Africa, East Asia and South America; for in these countries, until the last two decades, a high infant mortality rate, coupled with shortage of food and the prevalence of crippling infectious diseases, has acted to hold down the numbers of children reaching adulthood, and of young adults reaching old age.

In an individual lifetime, few of us will come across more than one or two persons of 100 years of age in our own social or even professional spheres. Physicians active in the practice of geriatrics (that is, the diagnosis and treatment of diseases and disabilities in later life) are more likely to encounter centenarians, and will certainly come across large numbers of octogenarians and nonagenarians among the patients they see and treat from year to year. Since the 1930s, countries like France, Sweden, Belgium and the North American states—as well as the United Kingdom—have seen a dramatic rise in the proportion of over-seventies in their respective populations. By 1970, they constituted ten per cent of the total population in each of these countries. Australia and New Zealand have had an even greater rate of increase in the proportion of old people.

By 1984, a year for which the late George Orwell predicted a severe political fate in the economically advanced countries, it is estimated that there will be more than 8 million senior citizens in Great Britain, that is, one retired adult for every four of working age. This figure will include about 900 centenarians, and about 400,000 people in their eighth or ninth decades. Official 1951 census returns revealed 750 centenarians in a British population of 50 millions. In the United States of America in 1950, the official figures showed 6,500 centenarians in a total population of 150 millions. New figures for the 1950s represent a ratio of centenarians to total population four times higher in the United States than in the United Kingdom and, although British census figures taken in 1971 are not yet available at the time of writing, there is no reason to suppose that these ratios have altered twenty years later. In both countries there has been equal success in reducing morbidity and mortality among infants and children, and diminishing disease and disability in adults and older people. The number of ageing people in all advanced countries has been offset by a reduction in family size (that is, an apparently diminished fertility) and the United States and United Kingdom have shared this trend. Again, life expectancy figures in the economically developed countries of Europe, Australasia and North America—and more recently in Japan and Soviet Russia—have risen steadily for both men and women, and are now at a peak of 70 years for men and 74 years for women. Life tables going back to the start of the twentieth century show, moreover, that compared with 1900, the chance of a 70-year-old's reaching 85 or over was three times better in 1960.

In terms of advanced longevity, however, the centenarian is still a member of a human elite. He or she has survived premature death from man-made dangers and natural disasters; any serious effects of local diseases or of epidemics, or even of pandemics, have been avoided; the physical and mental stresses of family life, work, social life and the environment have been weathered successfully; and the degenerative illnesses and physiological processes of ageing have been slowed, delayed or combated for a longer period than his or her contemporaries have achieved over the years. In Great Britain, the one hundredth birthday receives official recognition from the Crown in the form of a telegram from the Queen's private secretary offering Her Majesty's congratulations and good wishes. In other countries, the practice varies between official congratulations from the local government and parochial recognition from relatives, friends, societies and clubs. The local or national press soon gets wind of the centennial celebration of the senior citizen, and arrives with photographer to record the event. Inevitably, the centenarian is asked to which factors he or she attributes the remarkable record of years. The replies given and recorded reflect the whole gamut of individual life patterns: vegetarianism, gluttony, regular alcohol, abstinence, multiparous motherhood and celibacy are equally and oppositely proffered as pathways to longevity. Depending on the paper for which he reports, the correspondent may stress 'natural' living habits against materialist pleasures and synthetic joys, or uninhibited self-indulgence against the puritan ethic.

Readers' reactions to a news story about a centenarian reflect a mixture of uneasiness and admiration, or indifference and wonderment. Remarks like 'isn't she marvellous' contrast with 'hope I never reach that age', and 'all her faculties, still' with 'terrible, outliving your contemporaries'. These comments reveal an attitude to old age: as a personal calamity, or a marvellous opportunity—as a stroke of bad luck, or the height of good fortune. The pessimistic remarks notwithstanding, there is strong and persistent interest in human longevity. It may be considered in terms of factors which prolong life generally, or of factors which allegedly restore youthfulness, or of factors which maintain sexual potency into advanced age: these are the traditional searches for the 'elixir of life', rejuvenation and perennial sexuality, so vividly recounted in Alex Comfort's study *The Process of Ageing*.

Longevity can also be looked at in a less egocentric manner by the community, in the search for and discovery of significant genetic factors in health and disease which affect age. The social, economic and environmental determinants of survival into the eighties, nineties, and hundreds are also of interest and increasing importance; for as the proportion of very senior citizens rises in the community, there is increasing need to consider the quality and content of very senior life in that community. Social science informs us that very senior citizens in economically developed countries are not usually 'producers' but are 'specialised consumers'. This reflects an increasing dependence socially and economically on relatives, friends and neighbours, on local authorities and State bodies, and on the fixed income of pensions and personal savings. The extent of dependence would be expected to increase with each decade past seventy years but, as we shall see, there is no fixed ratio of number of years to degree of dependence. The material which is presented in the following chapters derives from case histories and population studies in many countries and different communities, apart from material gathered personally by the writer in his practice of geriatric medicine. Considering the evidence as a whole, the reader should find adequate confirmation of a statement made by Sam Ullman, the civic leader of the 1920s from Alabama, USA. Nobody grows old by merely living a number of years. People only grow old by deserting their ideals.

CHAPTER 1

Too Many Centenarians

THERE IS A WONDERFUL SEPIA-TONE PHOTOGRAPH WHICH CROPS up with unfailing regularity when a newspaper or magazine carries an article on human longevity. It shows twenty-two stalwart men, eight seated and the others standing, all dressed in the military coats, boots and hats of the Cossack style and all presenting smiling faces to the camera. The caption beneath the photograph usually tells us that this is a group of Georgians in the USSR, each of whom is a hundred years old or more. The group may be described as a troop of horsemen or a local male-voice choir. The accompanying article will tell us that Georgians have an enviable reputation for longevity and, moreover, are active in some form of work as well as enjoying leisure into old age. There may even be a story about one or two of these happy centenarians marrying for the third or fourth time—usually very much younger women.

Georgia, as a glance at the map of the Soviet Union will confirm, lies in the shadow of the Caucasus mountains, and is a remote state which has tended to be cut off from the mainstream of Soviet life for many years. This remoteness from civilisation on the modern scale gives us an obvious clue to the apparently high incidence of centenarians in the Georgian communities, and teaches us a useful 'sceptics rule'. The more isolated an area of population remains in an otherwise advancing country, the greater its claim for a high percentage of centenarians and very senior citizens. Hence the figure of more than two thousand centenarians in Georgia, USSR, must

B

be regarded sceptically even before we come to consider the
existence or otherwise of birth certificates.

It is not only the physical remoteness of a population group
which influences the claim for greater numbers of centenarians and senior 'runners-up'. Other factors include social
development, economic wealth and the presence or absence of
literacy generally in the population group. There is also the
factor usually described as 'absence of stress', which covers
both the absence of work pressures caused by the automated
and mass-production methods of industrial societies, and the
absence of the emotional problems of loneliness in cities.
Then, again, there is no smog or fog or excessive diesel fumes
or factory smoke to attack the lungs of Georgian peasants. By
contrast, we have convincing evidence that atmospheric pollution in industrialised societies considerably shortens lives.
John Fry, in his 1962 study of diseases of the respiratory system, reminded us of the great fog of London in 1952. This
menace of soot, smoke, dust and sulphurous emanations lasted
for four days at the beginning of December 1952 and was
responsible for an estimated five thousand deaths. Those who
died were predominantly in the middle-aged and elderly
population groups. On the other hand, peasant or poorly-in-
dustrialised communities like those of Georgia, or the emerging African states or the remoter South American countries,
have other factors that can shorten life. Diets deficient in protein and vitamins, extremes of climate, and the prevalence of
chronic infections (in the absence of proper hygiene and good
medical cover) may all have a quantitatively devastating effect
on such populations comparable to the pollution of the atmosphere in cities and towns.

COUNTING HEADS

We shall be looking in more detail at environmental factors
and advanced age in a later chapter. Keeping the above points

in mind, we can now consider the matter of statistics for the over-eighties and for centenarians in particular. In countries with enfranchisement of all citizens, we can look to the local electoral registers and gain some idea of the patterns of old age groups in local communities. The percentage of centenarians can then be estimated, and the ratio per thousand of population determined. By multiplying upwards to the national population figures, we can arrive at some idea of the total number of centenarians in a country. Statistical error is likely to be high using this method, however, because—among other reasons that will appear in due course—seaside resorts like Eastbourne in England or Miami Beach in Florida, and spa towns like those of the Netherlands or Germany have higher concentrations of senior citizens, attracted by the climes and amenities when they retire. P. Scott, in his study of the population structures of Australian cities in the mid-1960s, noted the tendency for very senior citizens to inhabit the older central parts of towns and cities while younger adults settled in newer suburban developments. A similar pattern was noted by S. Franklin in an earlier Australasian study of the North Island communities in New Zealand. An economic factor is also at work in the reverse direction since, as the 1951 census figures showed in Great Britain, richer old people do migrate to the newer suburban developments of many towns.

COUNTING YEARS: 95, 96, 100

The national census, which aims to cover every home in the country, recording voters and non-voters and inhabitants of well-populated and remote areas, gives a potentially much more accurate assessment of numbers of senior citizens. However, just as the physician taking a case history from a patient must always give that patient the benefit of the doubt of any statement he or she makes, so the census-taker must accept the declaration of age given on the census form. N. N. Sachuk of the Soviet Academy of Medical Sciences has evolved one method of 'spot checking' the accuracy of declared ages for people over eighty involved in a census. The method reveals a range of mistakes and confirms a theory of the present writer which we may call the 'custom of age increment', meaning that elderly men and women, particularly from the mid-eighties onwards, enjoy passing themselves off as older than their true ages. The 'custom of age increment' could be rationalised as a reflection of the older person's failing memory for some details, especially where brain function has been disturbed or lessened by hardening of the arteries that supply oxygen and glucose nourishment to the frontal lobes of the brain; but in fact mentally agile, well orientated octogenarians and nonagenarians participate happily in the custom of adding one to five years on to their bona fide ages.

Of course, genuine errors do arise because birth certificates have been mislaid, or because births have not actually been registered with the civil authorities. The latter was—and still is—likely to occur in remote areas and culturally backward countries. Also, figures of precisely eighty, ninety and a hundred may appear, because those countries with a long-established decimal system tend to encourage (tacitly) the use of figures rounded upwards. An extreme example, perhaps, of this decimal effect was noted in the 1948 census of the Philippine Islands when 16,000 centenarians were claimed in a total population of 19 millions. This would give an incidence of centenarians four times that in the United States. Even if we allow that a man or woman of 99 is in the hundredth year of life, the Philippines figures must be very inaccurate indeed.

THE THOMS TESTS: BORN, WED AND BURIED

As long ago as 1873, in a book on human longevity, W. J. Thoms set out the criteria which could be used to test the age

of a human being. The same criteria were confirmed thirty
years later in a book on centenarians by T. E. Young. For a
retrospective study, Thoms insisted on three main points:
proof of date of birth (by a certificate or by registration in a
local parish or civil district); proof of date of death (preferably
by certificate); and proof of name change in a woman (based
on a marriage certificate). Knowing of the not uncommon
practice whereby the son, or grandson, takes the Christian
name of the father, so that official records may unintentionally
transfer years of life from one to another, Thoms went further
in his demands for accuracy. He wanted proof that the second
generation child had not taken the birth date of the first
generation child. Here are three examples of centenarians
with offspring of the 'same name' which led Thoms to his
demand for the fourth kind of proof. David Grant, of Kinross
in Scotland, died in the year 1758 and was reputed to be 127
years old. John Mount, also a native of Scotland, died in the
year 1776 and was reputed to be 136 years old. Mrs Keith, of
Gloucestershire in England, died in the year 1772 at the
reputed age of 133 years.

By using his four criteria, Thoms was able to disprove the
extravagant claims of many centenarians to be, not just 100
years old, but 120 or even 130. Even this carefully tested
sociological approach however, led to a number of inaccur-
acies, so that Thoms tended to underestimate the frequency
of ages over 99 after all. Certainly he would have arched his
eyebrows in surprise at the photostats of a birth certificate for
a baby girl issued in 1858, set alongside the death certificate
for the same female subject who died in 1970. This was in
fact Ada Rowe of England who reached a clearly proven 112
years of age.

Thoms published his book on human longevity in Great
Britain, one year before birth registration in that country
became compulsory. Before 1874, it had been customary for
the British to make an official registration of birth, at least

since 1837. Unfortunately not everyone actually bothered to do so. In the United States of America there is a popular idea that official birth registration on that continent was stimulated by the American entry into the previously 'European only' World War I. Certainly before 1917 at least one in three American births does not appear to have been registered. (The native American Indians had their own calendar methods for recording the longevity of their chiefs, and of the chief's squaw. In Connecticutt, for example, Martha, the wife of a Mohican chief, Zachary, is recorded as having died at the age of 120 years in the year 1806.) Other countries such as France, the Scandinavian group, Canada, and Spain—where, like Great Britain, there had previously been parish or denominational registration of births—also introduced birth certification and, nowadays, it is virtually a universal practice for legal or statistical purposes. Those under-developed countries which had lagged behind the advanced countries in the recording of this particular vital statistic have had considerable stimulus to remedy the situation from the Statistical Commission of the World Health Organisation, since 1948.

At the other end of the scale, death certification was mentioned by Thoms as his second criterion. Deaths had been recorded on parish or religious registers or by local societies and ethnic groups from Biblical times—that is in both Eastern and Western societies, but Thoms wanted proof of, specifically, the date the person had actually died. This was because the records held dates of registration of death, and not necessarily dates of actual demise. It was not until 1874 in England that the signature of a qualified physician became compulsory on the death certificate. (Unfortunately, even at the present time of writing, a physician in Great Britain may sign a death certificate for a patient whom he has treated recently without seeing the body first.) Official state death certification is itself, therefore, not quite a hundred years old in Great Britain—and a much younger practice in other countries.

Advanced countries with a reasonable ratio of physicians to population have encountered few difficulties in registration of deaths. But in the under-developed countries with few medical practitioners, medical certification of all deaths has simply not been possible, and modified systems, using village chief, tribal leaders or local notaries, have been used. In terms of population statistics—such as those collected and collated by several United Nations bodies—this means that the information is incomplete, approximate and not easily interpreted. The result is liable to be a surprisingly high figure of very senior citizens compared with total population in reports, for example, from the eastern parts of Asia (but not Japan) and central African and some South American states; surprisingly, that is, in view of high infant mortality rates, low rates of expectation of life, and the problems of food deficiency, endemic disease, lack of sanitation and hygiene, all of which previously existed in the now advanced countries and apparently permitted very few over-eighties to survive.

As for the proof of name change in a woman by virtue of marriage registration, which was the third of Thoms's criteria—there were fewer difficulties here. At least this was so in those communities where surnames were clear, unequivocal and registered accordingly. In many countries of Europe, it was the call to Army service which forced the adoption of surnames where previously the man or woman was simply known as 'son of' or 'daughter of'. Once the practice of regular census enumerations began to spread from the Scandinavian countries during the later part of the eighteenth century, all developed and advanced countries demanded surnames of individuals. The situation has been more equivocal in under-developed countries especially in tribal communities, polygamous groups and in countries where the people have a regional name rather than a specific surname. Since, as we shall confirm again later, and have already noted in the Introduction, the female of the human species has a longer expectation of life than her male counterpart, there are many more women than men at the very senior end of life. Equivocal feminine 'surnames' can therefore, it seems, increase the incidence of eighty to a hundred year olds in such communities.

A good example of the surname problem Thoms was up against is the record of a London lady called Jane Lewson who died in the year 1816 at the reputed age of 116 years. According to one study, she was born in the Strand in 1700 during the reign of William and Mary of England. She married a very rich man and bore him a daughter, whose name was also Jane. She lived a very secluded life after she was widowed, attended by a few servants who, themselves, went through three generations in the same household. Apparently she never required medical attention and had an aversion to both fresh air and ablutions. Again unusually, she did not suffer with toothache but is said to have cut two new teeth at the age of 87. If we accept the records, she lived through the reigns of five British monarchs before dying in 1816 and being buried in Bunhill fields. The reader can decide on Thoms's criteria whether there was one very long-living Jane or two moderately long-living Janes.

Another example of this pattern was Rachel Bichois, of Rochelle in France. That famous town, besieged in the seventeenth century, saw the Protestant Rachel profess the tenets of the Church of Rome having been moved to do so by Cardinal Richelieu himself. She subsequently entertained, among other important personages, King Louis XIII. In time, she was the mother of no less than twenty-two children. Her year of death was 1710 and her reputed birth date was in 1603, which gives her a life of 107 years. At least one of this lady's many daughters was also called Rachel, however, so by Thoms's criteria we must be sceptical about her longevity.

A third example is the West Indian, Flora Gale, who was reputed to be 120 years old when she died in 1792. A free black lady from Savannah-le-Mer in Jamaica, she was said to be able to recall clearly in her ninetieth year the dreadful earthquake of 1692 which destroyed Port Royal. She, too, had a daughter, who was similarly named Flora Gale, which makes the student wonder about the possibility that this lady's marvellous recollection of the earthquake had been 'passed down' in vivid speech from mother to daughter—thereafter the vicarious experience seemed all too real to daughter Flora.

According to Alex Comfort, the distinguished gerontologist, the world record for authenticated longevity—within the acceptable physiological limits mentioned in the Introduction—is held by a French Canadian called Pierre Joubert. His death at the age of one hundred and thirteen and one third years is said to have been authenticated by the official statistician in nineteenth century Canada.

The Russian gerontologist Professor D. F. Chebotarev, president of the 9th International Congress of Gerontology in 1972, estimated that the over-seventies age group was running internationally to a figure of 112 million, and that this could rise to an incredible 120 million by the late 1970s. In a 1972 paper for the United Nations Educational, Scientific and Cultural Organisation, the professor indicated a figure of 25,000 centenarians in the world generally, with possibly four-fifths of them in the Soviet Union. This estimate was based on a figure of between 0.5 and 1.1 persons aged 100 per 10,000 population in economically developed countries: a statistic which Chebotarev mentioned in a 1969 paper to the 8th International Congress of Gerontology. Taking the lower ratio of 0.5, we should expect the 1971 British census to reveal a finite figure of at least 2,500 centenarians but this result is very unlikely, as we noted in the Introduction. It looks as if, even today, with our various criteria to follow, there is still a tendency to overestimate the world total of centenarians. With the over-eighties, however, we are in even greater difficulties since the number per 10,000 population in advanced countries now ranges between 15 and 65 per

10,000. The only certain fact is that the proportion of very senior citizens in all the populations of economically advanced countries continues to rise annually. This increase brings with it the critical social and economic problems of an enlarging group which is partially or completely 'non-working' and partially or completely on a fixed income for periods of up to thirty years or longer in each individual life. There is also the semi-related medical question of care and treatment of disease and disability in very senior citizens. These three issues will be considered in depth later in this book but points concerning them will arise from most of the topics we discuss.

CHAPTER 2

Heredity Factors—and Luck

LIKE FATHER, LIKE SON?

A WELL-KNOWN CHILD HEALTH SPECIALIST OF THE SCOTTISH school of medicine used to refer to the child, in its first twelve months of life, as 'this prototype human'. Although not the sort of phrase to use in front of doting new parents, the description served to remind his medical students that this primary model of human life would undergo many internal and external changes before developing into a fully functioning, independently mobile and active human being. This 'final' model is a product of both the effects of environment and the results of heredity. At the prototype stage, we can already identify some of the results of heredity, even if, at their simplest, it is merely a facial resemblance recognised by a delighted grandparent.

Every human body cell carries chromosomes in its nucleus. The chromosomes are microscopic rod-shaped material, forty-six in each cell nucleus (including two sex chromosomes which determine the overall masculinity or femininity of the human carrier). Arranged in lines along the chromosomes are the true holders of the hereditary elements, the genes, which are composed of a substance called deoxyribonucleic acid, or DNA. Abnormalities in offspring can be the result of disturbances in the chromosomes: an example is Down's syndrome in which the child is born with the physical and mental handicaps of mongolism. Variations in the genes, however, produce both normal and abnormal attributes in human beings. A normal attribute of red blood cells is that they can be grouped, for a given person, into one of four categories, O, A, B, and AB, depending on inherited genes. We can test a patient's red cells and discover to which group they belong; and, if he requires a blood transfusion, we are able to match them with blood from a donor who has the same group. An abnormal attribute of blood is the condition of haemophilia—in which blood fails to clot normally—and this depends on a gene carried on the sex chromosomes.

These particular genes and their effects are readily observed and recognised, because they are due to single gene pairs and their effect is abrupt: so many people are B group, so many A group, so many AB, and so many O. With many inherited characteristics, however, there is no clear boundary between one type and another. Rather there is constant gradation throughout the population from one extreme point to the other extreme point, with most people clustering around or near the average, and fewer people as one moves out towards either extreme. This type of distribution is known as a normal curve distribution. For example, if we determine the height of all adult mature men in the State of Arkansas, we can draw a graph matching the frequency (of men with a given height in centimetres) against the baseline of actual height in centimetres—and the result is a normal curve. This might show a peak at 178 centimetres (average for most men) falling quickly on individual families and especially on twins. The best- and 180, 182 and 184 to the right; that is, fewer and fewer very small and very tall men. The fact that height shows this normal distribution curve in a given population does not confirm, however, that inherited factors alone determine height. This can only be proved satisfactorily by carrying out studies on individual families and especially on twins. The best known study in families was made by F. Galton in England in the late nineteenth century, and further confirmation of genetic influence on height came through the studies of H. H. Newman (just before World War II) in the United States.

The genetic influence on longevity is not so clear. We cannot say with statistical assurances that, just as the offspring of small parents are likely to be small, so the offspring of parents who reach very senior years are equally likely to reach senior years. In the first chapter, we noted many of the difficulties in confirming the truth of claimed life-spans, particularly before official certification was established. This makes the study of long-lived human pedigrees more difficult in terms of authenticity—it is already problematical because of both the 'delay' before new generations confirm (or contradict) longevity and the lack of proper records in any case. In an unpublished book on British writers who lived in India, the Cambridge Fellow, Ian Stephens, drew attention to two families who appeared to illustrate that there is an inherited influence contributing to very long lives. Brian Hodgson, who died in 1894 at the age of 94 years, was 'the last of a succession of four men thus named, whose average age at death was over 83'. Also mentioned was Sir George Trevelyan who died in 1928 at the age of 90—his father, Sir Charles Trevelyan, died in 1886 at the age of 79 years, while his (George's) son died at the age of 86 years. In the case of the Hodgson pedigree we must ponder at the fact that four generations had the same name, and be circumspect in terms of Thoms's criteria. The Trevelyan pedigree, however, appears to be impeccable.

The influence (or apparent influence) of heredity on longevity is not confined to English families. In Sweden, for example, the Jernitz family had a physician grandfather who died at 104 years, a father who died having just reached his hundredth birthday, and several nonagenarian grandchildren. (Apparently the original Doctor Jernitz compounded an elixir which he passed on to his son and grandsons as contributing to a longer life. The real elixir may have been internal rather than external.) In Vienna, a family called Mazarella claimed a grandfather of 105, and father and son as centenarians—with at least one of the three long-lived members retaining most of his hair in its original black colour. (The most senior Mazarella died in 1774 before official certification was compulsory.) In Groningen, Holland, a family of fishermen all claimed long lives, to eighty or ninety; one of them, Peter Mauzere, is reputed to have died aged 109. Since he died in 1772 there cannot be adequate authentication, but the implication of heredity is there strongly. In Campbell County, Virginia, in the United States, a family descended from Charles Layne, who died at well over a hundred in 1821, has also had long-living sons and grandsons.

Eric Pfeiffer, a physician at Duke University in North Carolina, in the United States, carried out a longitudinal study on senior citizens to determine physical, social and psychological correlates in old age, for long-term (as against short-term) survival. We shall look again at this particular study in later chapters but, in terms of long-term survival, Pfeiffer did not mention longevity of parents or grandparents as a significant factor. His results were reported in 1969 but over four decades earlier, the American biostatistician Raymond Pearl had published his studies, in New York, on the biology of population growth, and on human biology. His work appears to confirm the impression gained from examples such as those above, that children of long-lived parents (and grandparents) are statistically more likely to reach senior years. Pearl worked at Johns Hopkins University in Baltimore, Maryland in the United States.

Another research worker at Johns Hopkins, this time at the School of Hygiene and Public Health, has followed the path set by Pearl (who died in 1940). In 1968 Dr Bernice Cohen was engaged in detailed studies of Baltimore families in an attempt to evaluate the influences of heredity and environment on the mortality patterns of those families. Actuarial calculations did seem to show definite correlation between a child's life expectation and the seniority in years achieved by his or her parents. Anyone who has applied for life insurance knows that the statement about personal health and history which has to be completed contains a 'family history' section. This questionnaire asks about the health of brothers and sisters (numbers alive and dead, and state of health or cause of death). Invariably the same questions are asked about the applicant's father and mother. Presumably, the premiums charged may be weighted up or down according to whether there is a 'bad' or 'healthy' family history and evidence of premature death or parental longevity.

PLANNED SENESCENCE

If the capacity to survive to senior and very senior years is, other things being equal, predominantly determined by a built-in genetic programme, then specialists in ageing and ageing research are dealing with a familiar problem. It is what Vance Packard first described, in his book *The Waste Makers*, as planned obsolescence. Packard was, of course, looking at material products of industry in the advanced economies of the West. In the human sphere, we should perhaps use the term planned senescence since, if there is a genetic timetable, it is revealed in the visible ageing changes—of skin, hair, movement, strength and mental function. The obsolescence analogy is a fair one, however, since Packard listed three forms of the condition: obsolescence of desirability, of quality and of function. We can consider in turn how each of these three states applies to the older human being in contemporary society.

In a youth-oriented era such as the 1970s, to be classified as 'old' is to be undesirable (or apparently so) in many social spheres. Theatre, cinema and many other forms of entertainment such as discotheques (although perhaps not bingo) are aimed at the young unattached and the young marrieds. New towns and suburban developments welcome the younger worker and his family but are doubtful or discouraging towards older employees and retired people. Cultural (but not usually ethnic) societies and local social groups often have an upper age limit, after which the member—however active or functional—must necessarily retire or resign. In human relationships, later life is thought to be a miserable and unromantic period because of the myth of absent sexuality among older people, and the diminished glamour of physical appearance— as well as the increased rigidity of outlook and loss of breadth of personality. In the economic sphere also, to be 'old' is apparently to be undesirable. Compulsory retirement both in shop floor and managerial positions, and in many professional occupations, reduces the status of the older individual to that of 'non-worker' in the community and non-contributor in the home. Even in the few years immediately before retirement, the employee is already at a disadvantage—for example, if he becomes redundant he has major difficulties in competing for new jobs with younger men, or if the firm goes over to new techniques he may find reorientation more difficult, or retraining more onerous, than a younger man. Once he has actually retired, there are the problems of living on a fixed income, whether on a state pension, or occupational pension, or on the interest from savings or on annuities—or on one of a variety of combinations of these incomes. If the retired old person is interested in finding part-time employment, he may have difficulties on account of age and be forced to undertake menial work well below his real skill or training levels.

In the case of obsolescence of quality, we find a more subtle set of innuendoes which follow from some of the problems mentioned in the paragraph above, and also from the assumption of diminished function. The quality of performance at work is thought to deteriorate in senior years—although there may be a grudging admission of responsible and conscientious application, loyalty and willingness, particularly in long-serving employees of an enterprise. The quality of judgement is also assumed to suffer in some settings—so that physicians, lawyers, civil servants, managers and directors are all pensioned off in the very years when they combine a wealth of experience with an abundance of knowledge. (Politicians seem to escape from this qualitative assumption: consider those three famous octogenarians of the twentieth century—Konrad Adenauer, Charles De Gaulle and Winston S. Churchill.) There is also the inference we have already discussed that the quality of life in older people is poor and unsatisfactory in comparison with younger age groups. This stems not only from the social and economic problems outlined above but from the greater health risks in senior years. Thus cardiac, chest and arthritic complaints are commoner in senior employees than in juniors, and convalescence to recovery is more prolonged. Furthermore, the incidence of disabling degenerative complaints like hardening of the arteries, blood clots in major vessels and wear and tear in joints increases steadily in the very senior years. Lessened mobility because of these complaints, and because of changes in balance and muscle power, tends to reduce the field of daily living and the total or global reception of faces, places and ideas.

Thus obsolescence of quality spills over into obsolescence of function, with reference to both individual internal organs —heart, brain and kidneys, for example—and the individual human being as an integral person. Emotion, intellect and memory—that is the psychic part of brain activity—are also seen to be altered or modified or actually to decline in output and capacity and resilience. The extent of such obsolescence of function—and of quality and desirability—we shall evaluate properly in due course. At this point, we can recognise that the sum total of these three factors may add up to an 'obsolescence programme in human biology' and that such a programme may be contained in the individual's genes. (For students of theology, the familiar notion of 'predestined

c

human pathways' appears all of a sudden to have a bioscientific quid pro quo—but this is not our present consideration.)

OLD BEFORE THEIR TIME

Before we go on to look at the various theories on the actual causes of ageing—the 'exciting' causes rather than genetic predisposition—there are some interesting heredity factors which seem to act against the possible longevity of the offspring. The result is premature obsolescence or senescence for the individual child or for several siblings. For example, the relatively rare condition of Huntington's chorea, characterised by grimacing, jerky movements and unsteady gait, comes on in the thirties or forties, in children of either sex where one parent is affected (an 'autosomal dominant inheritance' in genetic terms). The affected person, apparently normal in childhood, becoming choreic in early middle-age, goes on to develop premature dementia with impairment of memory and intellect along with personality change. Longevity is unusual, as death tends to occur ten to fifteen years after onset. Many life-shortening diseases in children, such as cystic fibrosis, Wilson's disease and phenylketonuria, are inherited from parents who are apparently normal clinically but are both carrying an abnormal gene that shows up in one quarter of the offspring (an 'autosomal recessive inheritance' in genetic terms). Certainly, informed readers will know that all three of these 'inborn errors of body function' are becoming amenable to various forms of chemotherapy, but they remain potentially life-shortening. In the case of rare recessive diseases, geneticists have noted that parents are more often consanguineous, so that first-cousin marriages may be higher than thirty per cent among the parents of affected children.

Children with severe abnormalities from birth (congenital defects) may have suffered from faulty chromosome transmission rather than gene faults. This may be related to the age of the mother, as for example in Down's syndrome (mongolism) in which at least one form increases in frequency (and risk) with the advancing age of the mother. Other chromosome faults which produce a combination of defects like deafness, poor vision and congenital heart conditions also have a higher incidence in older mothers (between one in six hundred and one in a thousand births). An extremely rare condition called progeria is characterised by growth abnormality and the appearance of premature ageing in childhood itself. There are few recorded cases in medical literature but there is a possibility that advanced age of father and (relatively) of mother may contribute to genetic programming for childhood senescence. There is a record of a Polish family called Krasiowna, of the village of Koninia in pre-Communist Poland, in which the parish registers show a marriage between Margaret Krasiowna and an octogenarian spouse, Gaspard. Margaret bore Gaspard two boys and one girl who all, according to the record, 'bore evident marks of the old age of their parents—grey hair, no teeth developing, sallow complexions, no strength, and all the external symptoms of decrepitude'. This is an eighteenth century record, but a very recent record of the findings in two patients with progeria was published by W. Reichel and R. Garcia-Bunel from the Gerontology Research Centre in Baltimore, Maryland, United States, in 1969. They confirmed that in progeria growth ceases by the third year of life and that all the organs and tissues show premature ageing.

The genetics of psychiatric conditions afford an example of an unexpected anti-longevity factor. True depressive mental illness (a psychosis formerly called melancholia) is one of the disorders of affect which are known to have a genetic predisposition. According to J. S. Price of the Maudsley Hospital in London, England, studies on twins have shown that variations in the predisposition to depression as an illness have a significant genetic background. There is a risk of attempted and successful suicide in cases of severe depression. This can act as a life-shortening (self-induced) factor in younger age groups. In older age groups, the commonest serious mental disorder is depression, so that patients of this type in senior years have a high (attempted and successful) suicide rate. Here then, albeit a little circuitously, we have another genetic factor influencing length of life. (For the record, in the United Kingdom in 1968 there were as many deaths by suicide as by road accidents. The latter are clearly a controllable cause of life-shortening. In the case of depression and suicide, there is an environmental influence as well as hereditary factors but neither is as easily controlled as traffic.)

Having considered the predisposing hereditary factors associated with, or antagonistic to, longevity, we can now look at the 'exciting' factors involved in the physical ageing process. These are hopefully more amenable to control than the mere luck of having parents and grandparents who pass on life-lengthening or life-shortening genes.

CHAPTER 3

Old Is the Opposite of New

HOW LONG IS A LIFE?

IN PARIS, FRANCE, M. FLOURENS PUBLISHED A BOOK CALLED *On the Duration of Human Life* in the year 1855, when the expectation of life for a newborn child was a mere forty years. No wonder his critics called the following description of life phases somewhat fanciful. The first period of manhood (as opposed to youth and childhood), he described as being from 40 to 55, and the second period from 55 to 70. The first period of old age, he further asserted, is from 70 to 85, and the second period of old age is from 85 onwards. A hundred years he assigned as the natural duration of human life. In the light of modern knowledge and a rising expectation of life, as well as the sharp rise in the number of over-eighties in the population, Flourens can now be seen as a kind of prophet, speaking ahead of his time. In the practice of geriatric medicine, physicians today have acknowledged tacitly that there are two 'age groupings', which may be called (in semantic discomfort) geriatric and elderly geriatric—the differences lying, among other factors, in the degree of dependence or independence at different decades.

The same Monsieur Flourens said in another part of his thesis that the true sign of completion of growth (of an animal or human) is the union of the shaft of the long bones (of the limbs) to their own bone ends. This union takes place at about the age of twenty in man, he declared, and man then lives to ninety or a hundred. Again, considering that Flourens wrote forty years before Roentgen discovered X-rays and radiology established when long bone growth ceases, his forecast was remarkable. The eventual union of the bone ends with their shafts occurs by the age of twenty-one, so that growth in height then ceases. Flourens drew the conclusion that when increase in height ceases, growth ceases generally throughout the body and ageing begins. He clearly considered that ageing took place at a lower rate and a slower pace than the growth process, if he was prepared to assign twenty years to full growth and up to eighty years for full decline. Once more, he was not very far out in his assessment although he could not (in the light of physiological knowledge at the time) realise how variable the rate downhill was for different organs and tissues. He did not understand either that certain tissues, such as skin, go on growing and replacing new cells as the old ones are shed, or that, while bone growth ceases in a linear sense, old bone is constantly being reabsorbed and replaced by new bone. Neither could he know then that certain tissues, such as the bone marrow which produces blood cells, and the blood cells themselves, may survive virtually unchanged in form and functioning to 100 per cent levels into advanced old age.

THE FIRST THEORY OF AGEING

All organs are made up of tissues with variable job functions in the day-to-day internal activities of the human body. The tissues in turn are made up of individual units or cells, with a definite chemical and physical structure in each cell, as well as a personal programme in the genes of the cell nucleus. The Dutch microscopist Antoni van Leeuwenhoek had first described the cell nucleus in the year 1700, and the anatomist Theodor Schwann put forward his cell theory of tissue function in 1838. These two developments led, not surprisingly, to the earliest known apparently scientific view that ageing was due to loss of 'life material' or 'vital substance' built into the cell. Each cell was endowed with a finite quantity of 'life material', possibly concentrated in the nucleus, and over a period of years the quantity was used up so that the cell degenerated and eventually died. No histologist or scientist actually managed to elucidate the nature of this life material although T. H. Huxley, a naturalist in Great Britain in the nineteenth century, described cell protoplasm as 'the physical basis of life'. As we noted above, the cells of a tissue like skin or blood are constantly being broken down and renewed throughout life. Red blood cells, for example, only last about one hundred and twenty days before becoming effete. They are removed from the circulation to be replaced by new red blood cells from the parent bone marrow. This clearly negates the basis of the 'life material' or 'vital substance' theory.

THE LIPOFUSCIN THEORY

In the last chapter, we looked at the rare condition of progeria, in which the infant and child suffer from premature senescence and have all the appearance of very advanced years on a chronologically young frame. In the two patients Reichel and Garcia-Bunel described, they noted an extensive build-up of a substance called lipofuscin. This is a pigment which can be detected by the process of fluorescent microscopy, and large accumulations of lipofuscin were found in the main organs—heart, brain, kidneys and liver—as well as in the gonads and suprarenal glands of the progeria sufferer. Pathologists who have carried out post-mortem examination of tissues in elderly persons have noted, in many cases, the presence of lipofuscin pigment in organs and tissues, and regarded it as a concomitant of ageing. In view of the progeria findings, however, it is tempting to suggest that senescence in any person (whether of the normal type or the accelerated form in progeria) is the result of a steady build-up of undesired and undesirable lipofuscin pigment, which progressively interferes with cell function and ages the cells, tissues, organs and ultimately the total individual. Unhappily for this theory, no positive relationship has been established between degree of functional loss and total quantity of lipofuscin (in a pigment form) in the cells of a given tissue.

In connection with this theory, a large pharmaceutical company in Great Britain has marketed an anti-lipofuscin preparation, meclofenoxate hydrochloride, in the form of tablets. Treatment with meclofenoxate has been shown to encourage the removal of lipofuscin from the brains of aged animals in the experimental laboratory. Experiments on the biochemical activity of brain cells in rats, mice and guinea pigs have shown that the addition of meclofenoxate stimulates energy processes and chemical function in such cells. In the human brain, arteriosclerosis (narrowing and tortuosity of the arteries) reduces the supply of life-giving oxygen to the brain cells of older people. This oxygen deprivation has been simulated in the experimental animal and apparently the action of meclofenoxate described above still takes place. The drug detail claims that up to eighty per cent of elderly patients who show slowing of brain processes in terms of memory, mood and intellect may show improvement on a course of meclofenoxate. Quite correctly, however, the detail advises that a satisfactory response to meclofenoxate is less likely where brain cells have decayed and where brain tissue has softened causing mental and physical derangement.

THE AUTO-IMMUNE THEORY

Another disease, somewhat less rare than progeria, has been used as the basis for a theory of ageing. The disease, Hashimoto's thyroiditis, occurs in adults, generally of the female sex, and is associated with the presence of protein material in the blood of the sufferers—material called antibodies. These antibodies are antagonistic to the cells of the sufferer's own thyroid gland, and cause disease and breakdown of thyroid gland function. The process is known as an auto-immune effect, which is explained as follows. At birth, there is present a built-in mechanism for distinguishing tissues belonging to oneself from those which are foreign or 'not-self'. This helps to make the individual immune to foreign material—such as bacteria—which is attacked and destroyed by antibodies. For some as yet unknown reason, this self-recognition of tissues breaks down in some individuals. Such people start to manufacture antibodies against the tissues in one (or more) of their own organs. An auto-immune theory of ageing would therefore conceive that, in a time variable for the individual and also variable for the tissues of that individual, there is a steady loss of the self-recognition mechanism. In time, the antibodies' attack results in the degeneration, decay and death of all the cells and tissues.

A possible corollary is that the development of hardening of the arteries, called arteriosclerosis, is due to an auto-immune process in the cells of the blood vessels. The speed of decay and degeneration in tissues and organs would be related in turn to the progress of auto-immune attack on the blood vessels, which supply oxygen and glucose nourishment. The immune process in the normal way accounts for the steady rejection of organs and tissues used in skin, kidney or heart replacements, in the dramatic transplant surgery of the past decade. Methods of delaying or suppressing the immune reaction in these tissue and organ grafts have been developed, such as the giving of cortisone, the injection of antilymphocyte serum, and the administration of antimetabolite chemicals, like methotrexate and cyclophosphamide. These have had a mixed success and are not without side effects of their own. As with drugs in the lipofuscin theory, an immuno-suppressive drug might be tried as an anti-ageing factor, to test out the auto-immune theory of ageing. So far, no evidence of anti-ageing action has emerged. However, Sir Macfarlane Burnett certainly included ageing in his concept of auto-immunity, and it is difficult to ignore for example, in studies of ageing skin, the presence of lymphocyte cells in frequent degree— and lymphocytes are known to be associated with the body's immune mechanisms.

THE SOL TO GEL THEORY

The supporting tissues in the human body, known as connective tissue, are made up of collagen, reticulin and elastin, and give support and resilience to skin, muscle, joints and various organs. A known feature of ageing is the change in the elastin content of connective tissue, particularly in the skin and especially in the skin of the face and neck. The elastin is chemically altered as the years progress so that it degenerates and 'disappears', accounting for the wrinkling of the face around the eyes and mouth and the sagging skin around the neck. Collagen forms the bulk of connective tissue and this too changes over the years, an important feature being a physico-chemical 'drying out' process. In colloid terms, this is described as moving from a 'sol' form to a 'gel' form. One theory of ageing has suggested this change from 'sol' to 'gel' as the primary change in all body cells, making them less and less active and functional. Alternatively, the 'sol' to 'gel' theory can be tied in with the hardening and tortuosity of blood vessels, so that this in turn produces ageing changes in the tissues and organs supplied.

THE ANSWER LIES IN THE CELL

We have noted how an 'information programme' is built into the cell, in the DNA (deoxyribonucleic acid) of the genes, which organises the production and distribution of proteins and enzymes in the cell body. The current theory of ageing was outlined by Dr Alex Comfort in an address to the 8th International Congress of Gerontology, in 1968, and again at the Zurich Conference on Control of Human Ageing in 1971. This views the ageing process as an 'information loss at the cellular level', and may either be the result of random damage to the DNA molecule, or an error in information feedback. Faulty protein production then occurs so that defective enzymes (promoters of chemical activity in the body) are released. The body, in turn, recognises the presence of faulty enzymes and calls for increased protein production. The feedback and programme produce still more faulty enzymes so that the cell ultimately dies, and so eventually does the organism. In this theory, we link up the genetic view of longevity, discussed in Chapter 2, with a genetic view of ageing. Experimental work in animals has been carried out and an error artificially induced, resulting in faulty enzyme production. The increase in protein production to compensate for the faulty enzyme output does occur in the experimental animal. Dr Comfort has now suggested as a model of the ageing process the long-playing gramophone record. This may become progressively scratched by constant usage so that the sounds become less and less easily understood. The rate of damage may be reduced, he says, by some form of 'lubrication'. Alternatively, if this record cannot be replayed once it has come to an end, he advises, we could run it more slowly to make it last longer (but not too slowly to reduce its intelligibility). At Zurich in Switzerland, Dr Comfort predicted the probability that, within five years, gerontologists and other scientists will begin major testing of 'slow down' methods for human subjects who are suffering from degenerative processes. When that happens and begins to be successful, we shall have to redefine 'old': not as the opposite of 'new' but as the comparative of 'very old'.

CHAPTER 4

An Arterial Puzzle

HARD LINES

THE ANCIENT BABYLONIANS HAD A SAYING: 'IN THE BLOOD IS THE source of all sickness'. A modern paraphrase of this aphorism might read: 'in the blood vessels is the source of all ageing'. For, without exception, the arteries of all human beings sooner or later develop the changes known popularly as hardening of the arteries, or medically as 'arteriosclerosis'. Arteriosclerosis reduces the supply to vital organs and tissues of blood containing oxygen and glucose and other nutrients. This produces a decline in function and structure of those organs and tissues and an 'ageing' effect is then present. The actual changes in the artery involve the three linings of the arterial tube: the muscle lining becomes thickened and the tube becomes stretched and irregular; the middle lining becomes harder, often having deposits of calcium in it; and the innermost lining becomes roughened and irregular (a porridge-like appearance) with yellowish material deposited on it. This third change, known as atheroma, results in a narrowing of the arterial tube, which depletes the blood supply to organs and tissues. A more sudden block in the flow through the artery can occur if blood clots over the atheroma deposits, closing off the tube.

V. Korenchevsky, one of the present century's outstanding pathologists in the field of human ageing, has carefully examined the whole question of arteriosclerosis. He has considered whether it represents a natural, normal degeneration—a physiological process—of true ageing, or an abnormal, unnatural change—a pathological process—which is not true ageing. The present view of both pathologists and practising physicians is that arteriosclerosis is a pathological and abnormal process, and that if it could be prevented or adequately controlled we would then see true physiological ageing in the organs and tissues of the body. The progress of arteriosclerosis is variable among individuals, and among their own organs and tissues. One sixty-five year old man, for example, may have much less evidence of hardened arteries than another sixty-five year old man in the same social and geographical group—and yet have much more evidence of hardened arteries than a third, seventy year old man in that group. Moreover, the first man may have the effects showing in his brain function, the second man may have effects showing in his heart function, and the third may be showing effects in his brain, heart and limb function. Any permutation of the results of arteriosclerosis can be found in the older man or woman, although there are certain well-recognised presentations. These may appear in different decades. For example, a salesman in his fifties complained, to his family doctor, of pain in both calves after walking five hundred yards. The pain was relieved by resting for a minute or two but recurred after another five hundred yards. In his sixties, the same salesman—who now had an indoor desk job—presented the new symptom of chest pain on going up stairs or walking uphill. Again this improved with rest but recurred on further effort. In his seventies, the salesman, now retired, complained to his doctor about his failing memory, particularly for recent events, and a tendency to emotionalism which he was unable to control. These sequential symptoms were the results of arteriosclerosis affecting first the arteries to his limb muscles, next the arteries to his heart muscle, and finally the arteries to the front of his brain. The symptoms and signs, given respectively the names

'intermittent claudication', 'angina pectoris', and 'cerebral insufficiency', represent the panorama of arteriosclerosis and are
not truly separate disease entities. The processes described in
the salesman were relatively slow and, to some extent, the man
and his body had time to adjust or even compensate for the
deficiencies of 'ageing' arteries. Unhappily, when sudden complete blockage of one or several arteries occurs, the organ or
tissue supplied may suffer irreparable damage, with death of
tissue leading to severe disability or even death.

HOW MANY VICTIMS?

L. Aschoff in the 1930s, H. Jellinek in the 1950s and L. Piggot
and T. Howell in the 1960s, working in Germany, Hungary
and Great Britain respectively, showed the rising incidence of
arteriosclerosis present in and contributing to disease and
death by carrying out post-mortem examinations of very senior
citizens. Jellinek's series of four hundred autopsies covered
the sixties to nineties age group, while Piggot and Howell's
series of forty autopsies covered the age range 90 to 99 years.
Jellinek found that the basic cause of death in fifty per cent of
his patients was hardening of the arteries, while the Piggot–
Howell group had a similar cause of death in thirty per cent
of cases.

These studies show very clearly how longevity can be
affected adversely by arterial degeneration in the senior age
groups. If we look at one particular form of this arterial degeneration, that affecting the arteries which supply the heart
—known as ischaemic heart disease—we find this is the leading
cause of death in all the advanced and developed countries.
The mortality figures in Europe alone show that ischaemic
heart disease causes almost a million deaths each year. It has
been estimated that, other things being equal, control and
prevention of arteriosclerosis in general—and ischaemic heart
disease in particular—in Great Britain could increase the life

expectancy at birth by about eight years in either sex.

MAKING MATTERS WORSE

Much research and experiment has gone on, both nationally and internationally, especially during the past two decades, to determine the causal factors in arteriosclerosis, and find out whether these can be influenced in terms of treatment and prevention. For example, certain illnesses are known to accelerate the development of arterial changes. Sugar diabetes, properly called diabetes mellitus, may affect the small and medium-sized arteries—in the limbs, producing poor circulation and reduced nerve function; in the eyes, producing defective vision; and in the kidneys, reducing kidney function. Smooth control of the diabetic state may prevent or delay the onset of such arterial changes. High blood pressure—'essential hypertension'—affects the medium-sized and large blood vessels. In the heart, hypertension accelerates the narrowing and increases the risk of clotting in coronary arteries, while in the brain, hypertension may speed up the narrowing and risk of clotting or haemorrhage of the brain arteries. Effective lowering of high blood pressure and control of the hypertensive state may prevent or delay the onset of these arterial changes.

The adverse effects of cigarette smoking on health generally have led to the British and American cigarette makers placing an 'official warning' about health hazards from smoking on each carton or pack. A report by the American Heart Association in the journal *Circulation* in 1970, based on prospective studies, showed a dose-related link between cigarette smoking and the incidence of, and mortality from, ischaemic heart disease. Inhalers fare worse than non-inhalers, possibly because of the higher level of carbon monoxide retained. The mortality rate in Great Britain continues to increase, although one group which appears to be going against this trend is

British medical doctors, many of whom have given up smoking in the last six years.

Obviously if there were a sharp decline in cigarette smoking in the general population, we might expect a drop in the mortality rate from ischaemic heart disease. But few heavy smokers find it easy to abandon the habit, despite the many and varied methods adopted to stop smoking. These include 'substitutes' like chewing gum, lozenges, sweets and chocolate, not to mention artificial cigarettes, lobelline tablets and sedatives or tranquillising agents. In Lancashire, England, a local public health department has set a much-copied example by organising periodically a one-week anti-smoking clinic, while individuals and organisations in the United States run Smoke Stoppers Inc. and Smoke Watchers International Inc. on a group therapy basis. The effort, in terms of both health and longevity, is worthwhile. Among the over-seventies, however, anti-smoking campaigns of any sort often fall on deaf ears. The senior citizen may take the short-term view, expressed in the statement of one of the writer's patients: 'if I can't have my smoke, doctor, it's not worth living until I'm ninety', as he coughed and spluttered through his sixteenth cigarette of the day. He was 81 years old. However, senior citizens with calf pains due to intermittent claudication, or chest pain due to narrowed coronaries, are more amenable to advice on giving up smoking—since the results are clearly apparent soon after doing so.

Apart from its effect on arteries, cigarette smoking may also have a more generalised ageing effect. Forbes, Wang and Robinson, of Canada and the United States, have shown how tobacco smoke contains a compound, benzpyrene, which may break down within the body cells to form 'free radicals'. The 'free radicals' are groups of atoms which do not readily decompose with, say, raised temperatures or other reactions, and which therefore persist and build up inside the body cells. Such 'free radicals' may be derived from ingested as well as inhaled substances. An additional theory of ageing views these 'free radicals' as contributing to the progressive damage to the DNA molecule, and hence to information loss at the cell level. If tobacco smoke contains such anti-longevity components, this is more useful ammunition for the anti-smoking lobby in all advanced countries.

LOW FAT, LOW CHOLESTEROL

If the anti-smoking industry is only just finding its feet and beginning to grow, the anti-fat and anti-cholesterol industry is well into young adulthood. Early experiments on animals showed that the change in the arterial lining (atheroma) could be brought about by feeding animals a high fat diet, which led to a high level of cholesterol in the blood. It was already known that people who suffered from a familial complaint with the essential feature of high blood cholesterol also suffered a higher incidence of atheroma, arteriosclerosis and ischaemic heart disease. In countries where the fat intake is mainly vegetable, and of the chemically unsaturated form, the level of cholesterol in the blood of the indigenous population is lower than in countries where the main source of fat is animal, and of the chemically saturated form. In 1957, H. Gordon and co-workers found that the levels of cholesterol in the blood of human beings could be lowered by adding unsaturated fats to the diet. Apart from vegetable fats, other useful sources of unsaturated fats are corn oil, cottonseed oil, safflower oil, soybean oil, sunflower oil and peanut oil. Even before any reduction in human incidence of atheroma, arteriosclerosis and ischaemic heart disease by taking unsaturated fats could be shown, the health foods industry, the vegetable fats industry, and the manufacturers of corn and other oils were all promoting their products in the 'war against heart disease and premature ageing'. Milk and milk products were 'fat-reduced' and were advertised as such, or as 'low fat'.

D

Both C. Tejada in 1968 and A. Keys in 1970 showed an important relationship between mean levels of cholesterol in the blood, as well as fat in the diet, with the frequency of ischaemic heart disease and the severity of arteriosclerosis. Although initial studies of low fat diets in heart disease in 1965 did not show encouraging results, people with cholesterol levels of 300 milligrams or over in the blood were recommended to use the unsaturated fats diet. Alternatively they took a chemical substance—called clofibrate—which reduced cholesterol blood levels. S. Dayton and co-workers, as well as O. Turpeinen, in the late 1960s published reports in the journal *Circulation* suggesting that the incidence of atheromas and arteriosclerosis diseases could be reduced by modifying blood cholesterol and dietary fat. More recently, reports by M. Oliver and H. Dewar of Great Britain, in December 1971, showed that clofibrate, which reduces cholesterol in the blood, has some kind of protective effect in patients suffering from narrowed coronary arteries that cause chest pain on effort.

Nevertheless, there is a lack of properly designed and controlled trials in the general population on the effects of long-term use of unsaturated or low-fat diets. John Yudkin of London, England, suggested in 1963 that the dietary factor that is the 'baddie' in the play is sugar. Sugar and other carbohydrates undergo purifying processes that tend to remove vegetable fats. Since sugar and carbohydrates have come to dominate the dietary scene in the developed and richer countries, this was suggested as the source of dietary mishap. In 1970, however, M. Crawford of Great Britain carried out reasearch which showed that animals could contain less of the saturated fat if the modern 'factory farming' of animals intensively reared was stopped, and 'free-living' growth of animals was permitted. Presumably then, our animal fat intake would no longer be harmful and a good deal of arteriosclerotic ageing would be prevented or delayed. It is common knowledge that obesity from any cause in human beings is harmful, and that overweight people have a higher incidence of arteriosclerosis in its various forms. Thus, any low-fat or cholesterol-reducing diet is necessarily part of a calorie-reducing diet, if it is to be at its most effective.

REMEMBER WHAT FEET ARE FOR?

There may be a further antidote to arterial change. J. Morris and M. Crawford, writing in 1968, considered that regular physical exercise and activity promotes the health of heart and blood vessels in the middle-aged community; and G. Mann and co-workers in the United States had already shown, in the late 1950s, that moderate exercise can reduce the levels of cholesterol in the blood. The popularity of active sports in advanced countries is certainly a product of being 'leisure-rich' but activities such as golfing and jogging, especially in the older age groups, are also influenced by the knowledge of the beneficial effects of exercise on the arteries and the heart. G. Rose studied English civil servants, and reported in 1969 that there was a noteworthy link between the duration of the daily walk to work and the frequency of ischaemic heart changes (as measured by the electrocardiogram).

One other factor which is said to contribute to hardening of the arteries and ischaemic heart disease is stress. This includes both emotional stress and environmental stress, acting together or separately. We shall be discussing the effects of emotional stress in some detail in Chapter 6. In the case of environmental stress, there is no doubt that extremes of climate—the cold extreme rather than the hot extreme—aggravate the narrowing of both limb and coronary arteries. Mortality from ischaemic heart disease invariably rises in frequency in severe winter conditions, and to a statistically significant level, as shown in the studies of P. Nordquist.

IS IT SAFE TO DRINK THE WATER?

Another environmental stress factor which has been implicated is the 'hardness' of the local water supply in certain communities. In 1960, for example, H. Schroeder of the United States carried out research on the treated water supply of many large metropolitan areas in the United States. Reporting in the *Journal of the American Medical Association* that year, he explained that there were 'highly significant negative correlations' between total hardness of the water and the presence of certain dissolved solids and elements like calcium and sodium, and deaths from heart and coronary artery disease. The implication is that soft drinking water is more dangerous than hard drinking water in environmental effect on the coronary arteries.

In the late 1960s, the Crawfords in England published comparisons of heart conditions in Glasgow, a city with a very soft water supply, and London, a city with very hard water. The main finding appeared to be evidence of more atheroma change in the lining of the arteries of young men from Glasgow, the soft water city. In 1971 M. Crawford produced further evidence from research in a number of British cities that hard water was a protective factor against heart and artery diseases. This thesis was challenged, however, in a report by G. Comstock in the *American Journal of Epidemiology* in 1971. Comstock reported a study within an area where different houses were supplied by water from different sources. The results did not show that people who had suffered 'heart attacks' were more likely to come from homes supplied with soft water. More research is clearly necessary before public health authorities can recommend the hardening of soft water as a pro-health, anti-ageing project.

CHAPTER 5

The Hormone Story

SEX HORMONES

THE DEVELOPMENT AND WORLDWIDE USE OF ORAL CONTRACEPtives (the 'pill') has made the notion of hormone substances familiar to great numbers of adults in contemporary society. Yet the idea of a chemical substance produced by cells in a gland in one part of the body and carried in the bloodstream to act on other parts of the body is already two centuries old. The French physician de Bordeu, who practised in Paris in the latter half of the eighteenth century, had been studying the eunuch as a medical curiosity. He conjectured that emasculation (by removing the testicles) must remove some substance, produced by the testicles, which had a 'male' effect on other parts of the body. This was the earliest recorded notion of male sex hormone, which we know now is produced not only by healthy adult testicles but also by the suprarenal (or adrenal) glands in the male adult (and to a lesser extent, in the female adult). Fifty years after de Bordeu's observation a neuro-physiologist, C. E. Brown-Sequard, suggested that semen itself might contain the 'effective substance'. He is reputed to have tried the injection of seminal fluid on himself in his own old age, presumably hoping to stem senescence or even turn back the clock. In late nineteenth-century Vienna, Eugene Steinach had experimented on animals using testicular grafts, but it was Voronoff who began the historically famous 'monkey gland' operation, in which healthy animal testicles were transplanted into ageing humans, to try and restore potency and virility. From what we noted in Chapter 3 about the body's ability to recognise 'self' and reject foreign material, we can assume that any apparent rejuvenation was short-lived indeed—or at best, psychological. In the first thirty years of the twentieth century, scientists in Germany and Switzerland isolated the actual hormones produced by the testicles—namely testosterone and androsterone.

On the female side of the picture, the ovaries—internal equivalent of the external male testicles—were shown to produce female sex hormone by the work of an Austrian physician, E. Knauer, though Steinach had also experimented in this direction. Further research by European and American workers revealed that the two basic chemicals produced by the ovaries were the oestrogen group and the progesterone group. Yet other research scientists showed that the anterior pituitary gland, a tiny piece of tissue in the brain inside the human skull, itself sends out hormones to act on the ovaries and testicles (and other hormone glands) to produce their hormones in turn. The whole system is a governor mechanism with feed-back effect, which keeps the hormone output levels stable.

FEMALE SEX AGEING

The discovery of the sex hormones was welcomed enthusiastically, not only by medical doctors interested in treating illnesses due to lack of hormones but also by those who believed that here at last was the 'secret of eternal youth'. The sex hormones in the adult woman control the recurring monthly cycle, in which the lining of the uterus is prepared to receive the fertilised human egg—and if it does not do so, the lining is discarded in the flow of menstruation. Menstruation ceases around the fiftieth year (or a few years earlier) in all women, regardless of race or geographical area. Thereafter the ovaries no longer produce the eggs for fertilsation, and the ovarian tissue degenerates completely into non-functioning material. With this ovarian shut-down, the female sex hormone production drops sharply (more so in some women than others) and the features of the menopause appear. These include physical changes, which increase as age progresses: loss of skin bloom, thinning of scalp hair, increase in facial hair, increased skin wrinkling, a tendency to sagging of the breasts, some thinning of the bones of the spine and limbs, and a drying and thickening of the lining of the vagina; and there may also be mental changes: nervous and anxiety states, increased introspection, mild or moderate depression, and a decline in sexual tension or libido. Both physical and mental changes vary in severity and extent, depending partly on the previous physical condition and personality of the menopausal women, and partly on the degree to which suprarenal gland production of sex hormones compensates for the shut-down of the ovaries.

HORMONE REPLACEMENT

These physical and mental changes, where troublesome or severe, can be helped by giving 'hormone replacement' therapy. This means the medical prescription of oestrogen (with or without progesterone) for a limited period, to 'tide the patient over the adjustment phase'. Some gynaecologists in the United States and in Europe have encouraged women to go on taking the anti-menopause hormones 'indefinitely' into the sixth and seventh decades of life. They have pointed out how such women maintain a youthful appearance of skin, breasts, hair and genital organs, which contributes to the psychological well-being and aesthetic physique of the individual. Other physicians have argued that oestrogens may be a 'provoking factor' in cancerous growths of the uterus. They also point out that oestrogen-progesterone preparations can

mask the irregular bleeding that identifies a malignant growth
in the uterus, because such hormones 'regularise' the bleeding. The doctors therefore advise periodic interruption of
hormone intake by those people taking anti-menopause hormones. (One way round the 'should we–shouldn't we' dilemma
of taking hormones after the meopause is to have regular
sampling of the cells in the uterus at a 'cervical screening
clinic'. Such cell samples reveal the extent of natural hormone
deficiency after the menopause, and also the presence of early
malignant change.) Of course the oestrogen and progesterone
hormones in women are not, after all, the 'secret of youth'
or the 'elixir of life' that the ancient alchemists and their
modern counterparts would like to have discovered. Once
the ovaries shut down at the menopause, they stay non-functional and there is no return to 'fruitfulness'. Neither do the
hormones reverse changes in the skeleton or delay degenerative changes in the blood vessels generally.

A number of studies in advanced age have now been undertaken to evaluate the possible beneficial effects of oestrogen
hormone administration in women. For example, the 'Golden
Acres' study, reported in 1969, by Dr Michael in Texas,
followed a three-year programme of therapy in fifty very
senior and senior citizens in an 'old age' home in Dallas.
Careful physical examinations against the risks of growth in
the uterus and breasts and cervical cell screening were carried out. A number of ladies 'dropped out' from the trial
because they found the uterine bleeding troublesome. Three
group aspects were examined at intervals during the therapy:
communication and interpersonal relationships, the degree
of self-care and of social responsibility, and work and recrea-
tional activities. The trial was a 'double-blind' type in which
the real hormone and a placebo (inert material) were given
in turn, without either the patient or the observers knowing
which was which until the 'code' was broken at a later date.
The only significant finding turned out to be an improved

adaptability in external functions in those old people who had been on the real oestrogens at the twelve months point in the study. Overall, there was no evidence of a generalised improvement in psychological and social aspects. Neither was there significant evidence of a slower decline physically and psychologically.

R. Hertz, a physician at the Rockefeller University in New York, has also reported on hormonal attempts to prevent senescence. His findings suggest that only the lining of the genital tract, in particular the vaginal mucosa, reverts to its normal functional status. He did not find that the sex hormones specifically ameliorate the ageing changes in other systems of the body or alter, for example, declining libido and depressive symptoms in very senior citizens. On the other hand, Dr J. Maddison of Teddington in England, who was a medical director of a geriatric screening and preventive clinic in Middlesex, United Kingdom in the 1950s and 1960s, used female sex hormones in old ladies attending the clinic. In an uncontrolled (that is, not double blind) trial of these hormones, he claimed—through clinical and photographic evidence—that such women showed improvement in physical tone, general health and external appearance. If the twin dangers, of possible promotion of malignant growths and an increased tendency to clotting of blood in arteries, can be overcome, we may see enthusiastic physicians prescribing female sex hormones to the over-eighties age group. For such women who feel that they wish to maintain a more youthful level of hormones in the blood, with the certain effect of keeping a moist and well-toned genital tract (and the less certain effects on other organs and tissues) daily hormone pills or periodic 'long-acting' hormone injection may become part of life in very senior years.

MALE SEX AGEING

There is no immediately comparable 'male menopause' in terms of a shut-down of testicle function at a given age. Instead the sex hormone function, and, with it, male potency, wanes gradually in the seventies and eighties, although claims for potency and the ability to produce reasonably healthy sperm have been made for nonagenarians and even centenarians. For example, the parish records of Inch in Wexford, Ireland, mention Henry Grosvenor who reputedly died at the age of 115 years and 'took his last wife' at the age of 100, 'proving an agreeable companion' and 'being well-preserved'. That was in the eighteenth century, when another senior citizen, 91 year old Lewis Galloche, a Parisian painter and chancellor of the French Royal Academy, was alleged to have retained 'the full use of all his faculties' until just before he died. In the early nineteenth century, another Irish centenarian recorded as having seven known wives, and producing children by all of them, was John Leary of Limerick. He sired a child in his ninth decade. Moving on to the twentieth century, the physician Dr Kenneth Walker recorded the observation of active sperm in the semen of nonagenarians. With ageing, the semen certainly thins, due to lessened secretion from the seminal vesicle and prostate gland. Moreover the force of ejaculation at intercourse diminishes and the total ejaculate is reduced to one or two millilitres (from about four millilitres in young adults).

THE TESTOSTERONE TREATMENT

As with oestrogens in women, so the discovery of androsterone and testosterone in men led to the use of male sex hormones in 'rejuvenation courses', or to try and slow up the ageing processes in different tissues and organs. With ageing, the tissues of the testicles gradually thicken and become less and less functional. There is a steady fall in male sex hormone output and an associated general weakness and apathy. There is also loss of sexual tension and sexual desires, with difficulties in erection and ejaculation. Unhappily there is no simple test, like the 'cervical cell screening' that can be done in women, to assess the amount of male sex hormone that is deficient. A chemical test on a twenty-four hour collection of urine can be carried out in the laboratory. This measures the output, excreted in the urine, of a substance called 17-oxosteroids. (These 17-oxosteroids measure not only male output from the testicles but also output from the adrenal or suprarenal glands.) In men suffering from apathy and impotence in senior years, the presence of a low figure for the 17-oxosteroids is a medical indication for a trial of testosterone—either as tablets in the form of fluoxymesterone or as 'long-acting' testosterone implants.

A number of trials have been reported, including a long-term study by T. Reiter in 1963. Some doctors have added small quantities of female sex hormone to the male sex hormone, suggesting that since this more closely resembles the 'natural' picture, success in therapy is more likely. The evidence, in general, shows an increase in overall well-being, with reduction of apathy and depression, and weight gain as well as gain in strength. These improvements far outweigh any sexual gain, in terms of libido and potency, especially in very senior citizens. There is no 'youthful recovery' in the testicles themselves and no holding back of the general ageing processes. Some medical doctors have considered giving anterior pituitary hormones in order to stimulate the testicles to produce more testosterone. This has not really proved successful because of the ageing changes in the testicles themselves. It may be that, as A. Hedri of Zurich University in Switzerland has pointed out in another context, the psychological and social stress levels of older men produce severe body-system disturbances. In that case, an 'ageing' symptom

like impotence may respond just as well (or better) to psychotherapy as to hormone injections.

OTHER HORMONES

There are other hormone-producing glands in the human
body, apart from the sex glands, whose shut-down through
illness or ageing can affect the over-eighties. For example,
sugar diabetes due mainly to disturbance of insulin hormone production from the pancreas may accelerate 'ageing'
changes in the blood vessels and nerves of many organs.
Vision changes, balance, and circulation in the limbs—already
perhaps deteriorating in the seventh, eighth and ninth decades—worsen appreciably with uncontrolled sugar diabetes.
One of the commonest hormone disturbances is failure of
thyroid hormone production from the thyroid gland in the
neck. Known as myxoedema (or hypothyroidism), the condition mimics all the signs of 'old age' even though the illness
can also occur in young adults. Because ageing changes may
already be present in the senior citizen, myxoedema is harder
to recognise and may well be missed for a long time until it
becomes severe. Typical changes include thinning of the scalp
hair, which becomes dull and lifeless, and drying and thickening of the skin. The sufferer always feels cold and tends to
sit over the radiator or other heat source, and be over-clothed
for the time of the year. The voice becomes hoarse and hearing
deteriorates. The mental processes become slow and dulled,
and movements are sluggish generally. Constipation is a common complaint in the illness, and there is loss of libido, and
general lethargy. To the non-medical observer, these features
are 'obviously due to ageing' and, since the process tends to be
gradual, even the regular family physician may not appreciate the lack of thyroid production—and may say 'it's just her
age'. The complaint of myxoedema is commoner in women
than in men. Treatment in the uncomplicated case (for some

are due to deficiency in the anterior pituitary gland) is the giving of thyroid hormone. In senior and very senior citizens, the treatment with thyroid hormone has to be commenced in very small doses, and built up gradually and carefully. Thyroid hormone is a powerful stimulant to elderly body systems, especially the heart, and the body must not be 'speeded up' too quickly in treatment.

Because of its role in promoting activity of all the cells in the human body, thyroid hormone has also been considered as a drug to 'reverse' ageing or 'hold it back'. In fact, reversal of the features described above only occurs in people who truly lack thyroid hormone production. Even then, if the condition occurs in the eighty or ninety age group, they will only revert physically to what they would have been like at that age if no hypothyroidism had ever been present. In terms of return to a reasonable state of health and some measure of social independence, treatment of thyroid lack even in a very old person can be very worthwhile. For example, a Dutch woman, J.M., aged eighty-eight, lived in an apartment in a four-storey building in a purpose-built area for housing the elderly, in Amsterdam. When seen by the medical doctor, she gave a history of difficulty in walking, due to a feeling of unsteadiness and physical weakness, for the previous three years. She had become confined to bed, become apathetic, and showed many of the features of lack of thyroid described above. She had begun to be incontinent of urine, too. In this state, she could no longer live alone or manage the apartment or reach one of the 'communal' dining rooms—and seemed likely to die. Other residents in the building confirmed that, up until about four years before, J.M. had been very active for her age, cheerful and interested in social conversation.

She was transferred to a hospital in the neighbourhood, given a fuller examination and then slowly started on small doses of thyroid hormone. Over the next six months she made a slow but steady recovery. She was able to return to

her apartment and began to renew her interest in her neighbours and their daily activities. The only problem that did
not resolve very well was the sluggish nature of her bowel
movements—but she admitted to very many years of constipation requiring various aperients.

Another example, J.T., a widower of eighty, lived in a
room in his sister's house in Berkshire, England but paid
rent and lived as a 'separate' body in the house. He went
out for his meals and did his own chores and looked after
the cleanliness of his room. The room was heated by an electric fire. The sister began to notice a definite rise in her
electricity bills and complained that, whenever she went to
her brother's room—even on warm sunny days—he always
had the electric fire on. She noticed he was becoming slower
over a period of eight months and not keeping the room clean
and tidy. Conversation was increasingly difficult as he seemed
slow to understand what was said to him—he was becoming
very deaf. She called the family doctor to see her brother,
after he took to his bed for a week and refused to come out
of it, eat, or bother with his hygiene. The doctor had not
recognised the lack of thyroid but told the sister her brother
had become 'very senile' and would require to be admitted
to a chronic ward in a mental hospital. Before anything could
be done about that, the old man became drowsy and then
comatose and was admitted to a medical ward as an emerg-
ency.

He was seen by the physician in geriatric medicine who
diagnosed the problem as severe lack of thyroid. J.T. hovered
on the brink of demise for some days, then gradually res-
ponded to the warmth, care and drug therapy which included
increasing doses of thyroid hormone. He spent five months
in hospital and then, as he did not appear well enough to
return to his sister's home to live independently in his room,
he was given a place in a residential home run by the local
authority where he settled in happily for a time. Physically,

he was frail but able to move about on his own. Mentally he became much more cheerful and exchanged gossip and stories with his own and the opposite sex in the home.

The 'hormone story' in very senior citizens does not end at this point. We shall be looking at hormones in the matter of stress and physical resistance in several other chapters. There is no doubt, however, that the curiosity of de Bordeu has unexpectedly helped more old people to reach advanced years, and to enjoy better physical health, even though hormones have not, after all, proved to be the elixir of life.

CHAPTER 6

Stress and Distress

ADRENALS AND ADAPTATION

THE ADRENAL GLAND—ONE LIES ABOVE EACH KIDNEY IN THE human being—has been said to resemble the two homes of a semi-detached house arrangement in an English suburb. Although close neighbours by the juxtaposition of their residences, the people in the families of the semi-detached homes lead separate lives. They issue forth each day into the working environment, barely acknowledging each other's existence—unless, for example, a mutual danger such as fire or flood threatens their homes. Then they may act co-operatively with their separate forces. The adrenal (or suprarenal) gland is divided, like the semi-detached house, into two separate 'homes', the adrenal cortex and the adrenal medulla. The cortex and the medulla produce separate sets of chemical hormones, which are unconnected in the ordinary way. But both sets may be produced at the same time as a 'co-operative' response to a mutual danger, that of stress. The hormones produced by the adrenal medulla are called adrenaline and noradrenaline (or epinephrine and norepinephrine, in the American usage). These chemicals pass from the adrenal medulla directly into the bloodstream, in response to external dangers or stress. They create in the individual body a state of 'acute awareness' and being 'ready for anyone or anything'. Physiologists describe this as the 'fight or flight' response: the heart rate speeds up, the blood pressure rises, the breathing rate increases, the hair 'prickles', sweating occurs, the pupils dilate, the sphincters contract, and the blood supply through the coronary arteries to the heart is increased. (The sympathetic nervous system is also involved in this 'fight or flight' process.)

The adrenal cortex produces several different hormones, with a variety of actions on organs and tissues in other parts of the body. In terms of reaction and resistance to stress, the group of hormones known as cortisol (and its analogues) is of primary importance. Increased cortisol production from the adrenal cortex occurs in the normal, healthy person exposed to the shock of accident, injury or bleeding. Severe heat and excessive cold cause a similar outpouring of cortisol, and so do poisonous substances and germ infections. Administration of anaesthetic gases and injections, and breathing in atmospheres with diminished oxygen content, also stimulate cortisol secretion. Not only physical events but also psychological states can stimulate its production, so that excitement and fear, anxiety and frustration, anger and pain are all 'mind' reactions which act on the body's adrenal function. In fact, the physical stimulus to cortisol production may be channelled through the emotional effect.

Nearly twenty years ago, the brilliant physiologist Hans Selye, working in Canada, presented his hypothesis known as 'the general adaptation syndrome'. The anterior pituitary gland in the skull sends out hormones which control other glands, like the thyroid, and regulate their production of gland hormones. Among its functions is control of the adrenal cortex production of cortisol through its 'governing' hormone ACTH (adreno-cortico-trophic hormone). There is constant 'feedback', so that as more ACTH is produced, more cortisol is produced; as more cortisol is produced, less ACTH is produced; as less ACTH is produced, less cortisol is produced; as less cortisol is produced, more ACTH is produced —and so on.... Part of the brain, the hypothalamus, is concerned with various body function controls—hunger, appetite,

E

temperature, sexual function, but especially with emotional changes and, via chemical agents, with the function of the anterior pituitary. Selye stressed the importance of an intact link-line, called the hypothalamic-pituitary-adrenal axis, in maintaining the human equilibrium through stressful states.

Several diseases in human beings can interfere with the production of ACTH from the pituitary, or cortisol from the adrenal gland; Simmonds disease and Addisons disease are two examples. The effects of these diseases on the body include thinning of the hair, poor resistance to cold and impaired resistance to infection. They also cause slower recovery from illness, muscle and skin thinning, general weakness and fatigue. Such features resemble the picture of 'ageing' in very senior citizens, which might suggest that in such cases there is invariably a disturbance of the hypothalamic-pituitary-adrenal axis. Animal studies, such as those of C. Rolsten in Ohio, United States, have suggested a possible decrease in axis response and activity with increasing age levels. N. Cartlidge of Great Britain, and co-workers, have examined the pituitary function and response in otherwise reasonably healthy patients between the ages of 80 and 95 years, and found these to be within the normal adult range.

There are two ways of looking at such a result. It may be that one of the reasons why the very senior citizen has reached advanced chronological age is the presence of an intact hypothalamic-pituitary-adrenal axis which continues the individual aged person's resistance to stress. On the other hand, it may be that the aged person's stress-resisting axis has been subjected to less or minimal stress, environmental and emotional, in his or her life (compared with younger, shorter-living individuals who have had excessive stress levels).

STRESS DISEASES

A number of diseases have been considered, over the years,

to be induced by, or related to, stress and stressful events. Sugar diabetes, for example, often appears symptomatically for the first time after some stressful situation, such as a bereavement, or some stressful illness, such as a chest infection, or even after an accident in the home or on the road. Since almost half the diabetics in the advanced countries are first diagnosed after the age of fifty, this might suggest that the anti-stress axis is less effective in older people, where there is also a predisposition to certain illnesses. (The reverse picture is seen in the condition of peptic ulcer, in stomach or duodenum, in which stress is thought both to provoke the ulcer, and to help maintain its presence. Because the stomach produces less acid and pepsin with ageing, any failure of the anti-stress axis in older patients does not reveal itself, since the predisposing causes are absent or slight.)

Excess production of thyroid hormone by the thyroid gland in the neck—called thyrotoxicosis—often appears after stressful events or situations, as with sugar diabetes. Since there is no apparent decline in predisposing factors with age, thyrotoxicosis can be found in senior citizens. Both sugar diabetes and thyrotoxicosis, left untreated, would be life-shortening in a significant way. Treated patients, however, respond well on the whole and part, if not all, of their original life expectancy can be restored, provided control is good and therapy effective.

In Chapter 4 we mentioned the possibility that stress speeds up the ageing process by promoting hardening of the arteries. In the case of emotional stress, however, good solid evidence of a direct effect towards arteriosclerosis has not yet been forthcoming. One of the problems lies in the gauging of supposedly stressful situations, and the other in measuring the emotional response of a particular person in that situation. In his own clinical practice, the present writer has noted certain events which upset—in terms of anxiety or even depression—senior citizens, and can therefore be considered stressful.

These include the act of advising admission to hospital, an
unexpected need to transfer the patient from one hospital to
another, admission to hospital itself, and discharge from hospital after becoming 'established' there (about three to four
weeks after admission). Further anxiety-provoking events are:
advice about the necessity of entering an old people's home,
actual entry to an old people's home, transfer from old people's
home to hospital, and transfer from familiar surroundings
(home and street) to new surroundings, for example because
of re-development of housing, or road widening. Distress in
the last case is likely to stem from a fear of social isolation.

ANXIETY

An important Australian study reported by E. Harwood in
1969 was carried out on a group of senior citizens whose ages
ranged from 60 years to 94 years. Using Cattell's Anxiety
Scale questionnaire, the research aimed at assessing 'normal'
anxiety levels which existed *per se*, and which might affect
other aspects of test performance. A 'control group' with an
age range of 16 to 25 years (that is, a group of teenagers and
young adults) was also studied, and the resulting scores compared with those of the senior citizens. Both open and hidden
anxiety scores were assessed. If these two forms of anxiety
were combined, the score for the senior citizens was significantly lower than for the teenagers and young adults. Young
women, especially, showed higher anxiety scores than those in
their senior years, and women generally showed higher anxiety
scores than men except around the age of sixty.

The Harwood study suggested that situations which may
provoke anxiety in younger adults are not stressful in senior
citizens, presumably because of adjustments made in ageing.
The study also confirmed that change of domicile tends to
provoke anxiety or depression, and that other stressful events
for old people are 'changes in public transport', and 'aware-

ness of deterioration' in such faculties as hearing, vision and circulation.

Since personality type must have some bearing on ability to cope with stress, the study also scored the groups on the basis of Eysenck's personality inventory. Two main streams were assessed, namely neuroticism and stability, and extraversion and introversion. In the senior citizens group, both men and women showed less extraversion or more introversion, and there was an important tie-up between the degree of anxiety and neuroticism in the older persons.

In 1959, H. Persky and co-workers in the United States showed that in anxiety, the sufferer has an excessively active adrenal cortex. Not only is cortisol produced in greater amounts but it is also chemically broken down and used up more quickly than in the non-anxious person. The Cartlidge study of the anterior pituitary function of healthy old people showed intact responses. Although there was no assessment of 'anxiety rating' in the group studied, the statement that they were in 'normal health' can be taken to include mental health. It would be of considerable interest if they had, in fact, suffered from chronic anxiety, for if we recall the feed-back mechanism—more cortisol production, less pituitary ACTH production—then we should expect the chronically anxious person in senior years to have an overworked 'aged' pituitary. This, in turn, might produce premature 'signs' of ageing such as weak and thin muscles, general fatigue, thin hair, and poor resistance to cold and infection, for example. However, Calloway and co-workers in the United States carried out a series of autopsies on senior citizens and found no significant age change in the pituitary. Moreover, as M. Friedman and M. Green have carefully pointed out, relatively few reports of adrenal and pituitary disease in senior citizens have been made in medical literature to date.

Friedman and Green studied hypothalamic–pituitary–adrenal function in well and mentally normal persons of both sexes with a mean age of 81 years. They again confirmed no evidence of decline of function or reserve capacity of the axis in response to 'stress' tests. They did note, however, that a number of elderly people had a much greater response to pituitary ACTH (given by injection in the test) so that more cortisol flowed from the adrenal cortex than in young adults. Moreover, the normal midnight output of cortisol in older people was found to be much higher than in young adults. Both these unusual results might be explained, according to the researchers, by a low output of ACTH by the pituitary and then a slow breakdown and use by the body. This, in turn, means that in some elderly persons the pituitary 'ageing' is really only a gland working in low gear—but still ready to change up to high gear and accelerate.

Apart from the effect of stress on the adrenal cortex, we have mentioned the 'fight or flight' mechanism of the adrenal medulla by its output of adrenaline and noradrenaline, known collectively as the catecholamines. M. Carruthers of Great Britain and P. Taggart and W. Sommerville, also of Great Britain, have suggested a link between the short-term effects of the rise in blood catecholamines in stress, and the long-term effects of atheroma changes in arteriosclerosis in the arteries. It is pointed out that in the non-exercising, heavy smoking, over-eating city dweller, there are frequent stress situations which cause sharp bursts of catecholamine production. The catecholamines have been shown experimentally, in animals, to produce a rise in free fatty acids in the blood. These are converted to substances called triglycerides, which are then deposited in the walls of the arteries, contributing to atheroma.

The effects of catecholamines in human beings have been confirmed, for instance, by examining racing drivers before and after the adrenaline-provoking stress of a race. If we extrapolate this kind of evidence to other drivers of public transport and private transport, we can begin to imagine the effects of car breakdowns, traffic jams and the general strain of road commuting on the arteries of today's driver. For the non-driving senior citizen, however, the stress is on the 'other foot'—the result of crossing roads and being a pedestrian today.

DISASTER

The effects of 'group stress' have always been taken for granted: London people in England during World War II subjected to 'blitzkrieg bombing', Japanese survivors after the Nagasaki atomic blast, Jewish survivors of Nazi concentration camps, East Pakistanis after the great floods in the early 1970s, for example, were all thought to show both immediate and remote effects in terms of physical disease and emotional or psychotic illness. The studies by H. Beach of Canada, and G. Baker and D. Chapman of the United States, as well as J. Morris and R. Titmuss of Great Britain, have confirmed this assumption, and the reality of the association between such major disasters and subsequent ill-health. C. Parkes pointed out, in particular, that the incidence of mortality and sickness is much greater —in the disaster group—over the first year following the disaster, than would be anticipated by mere chance. G. Bennet in 1968 studied the effects of severe flooding in the town of Bristol, England, on the subsequent health of the inhabitants. The follow-up assessment went on until 1970. Bennet again confirmed the significance of the post-disaster twelve month period: the health of the people who had been flooded was significantly worse than the health of those who escaped flooding. In particular, the over-sixties age group showed a statistically significant increase in the likelihood of demise within the twelve months after the flood.

Bennet's study is a contemporary reminder that both natural disasters and man-made disasters can adversely influence longevity, especially in senior citizens. Exactly how this influence works is not completely known. Even the most stable personalities, with no previous history of mental ill-health, may show a reactive depression following their rescue from a particular disaster. Those who have had previous neurosis or psychosis run more risk of a severe depression—with the possibility of attempting suicide. The effects on the tissues and body organs are less easily explained, for both the adrenal cortex mechanisms and the adrenal medulla mechanisms tend to be 'immediate' or 'very short term' in their hormonal effects. It is possible that a stress effect may unmask an illness that is 'simmering' but has not yet revealed itself in a significant way. Moreover, illness that is already present can be worsened by 'shock' and 'collapse' under the stress of disaster.

The idea that 'female hormones' are protective in some way was suggested by Bennet's overall age findings in men and women. He reported that the decline in physical and mental well-being and the presence of health disturbance was, in statistical terms, significant for men of all ages in all the circumstances recorded. In the women of all ages studied, however, the picture was different. While the women did show an increase in disturbed mental and physical health, this was not to a statistically significant level. Neither Bennet nor any of the other students of the effects of disaster on health has suggested the possibility of measuring cortisol levels and androgenic levels in both sexes, in the post-disaster twelve month period. This might help to assess the 'sex difference'. No one, so far as the present writer knows, has tested the notion of giving female sex hormone 'therapy' to post-disaster victims in the 'at risk' group (older citizens, ill citizens), although it would be as logical as giving female hormones to men with cardiac disease (because women before the menopause have a much lower incidence of heart troubles). This *has* been tried, unfortunately with no success.

However, the sex difference in reaction to disaster stress may lie, not in the hormonal make-up, but in the form the reaction takes. The tendency appears to be for women to react with mental signs and symptoms, and men to react with physical signs and symptoms. (The work of C. Parkes of the United Kingdom on post-bereavement illness shows a greater occurrence of mental reaction in women than in men.) Since post-disaster victims are likely to be given suitable sedatives and tranquillisers for a prolonged period, the mental symptoms are more likely to be kept under control than any physical changes that are taking place.

By definition, disaster is a stress that affects longevity in a way that is difficult for the individual to counter. Bennet suggested that the 'socially integrated' person is less likely to be at risk from the remoter effects of disaster. Presumably, therefore, married persons, persons in a neighbourly community, and persons with regular visitors and friends have a better chance of warding off the remoter anti-longevity influence of disasters. The lonely, the isolated, the widowed, separated or single person, is at greater risk—and this risk is apparently increased by belonging to the older, senior citizen age group. These thoughts are worth keeping in mind in our 'environment for age' discussion in a later chapter.

CHAPTER 7

Fat Man—Slim Years

FRESH AND NATURAL

THE NINETEENTH-CENTURY ENGLISH FOOD 'EXPERT', JOHN ABER-
nethy, made many judgements about health and eating. A
good example was his pithy statement that the 'object of
eating ought not to be exclusively the satisfying of the
appetite'. He insisted that the chief objects of feeding are
nourishing the body frame, appeasing hunger and then satisfying the appetite. Moreover, he advised—particularly for
older people—that portions of food should be small and taken
regularly. This was a brave statement at a time when gluttony and excess were common among the wealthier classes,
and food was scarce and expensive among the working and
peasant classes. Another writer on food and health of the
same period, Sir John Pringle, would have been most impressed by the current return to the eating of natural, organic
and non-processed foods among many of the younger generation in advanced countries. Pringle, for example, called honey
(used on bread or not) the 'juice of life' for aged people.
This enthusiasm for the nectar of flowers may have been
drawn from the ancient Greek interest in honey. Pythagoras
is said to have confirmed honey as the source of his excellent
health in advanced years, while the philosopher Democritus,
a reputed centenarian, said he lived so long by 'the application of oil without, and honey within'.

Contemporary interest in diet and its effect on health

stems from several directions. There is the familiar Malthusian worry that the increasing populations of both hemispheres—combined with improvements in socio-economic and health conditions—will steadily outstrip the available food supplies on a regional (if not global) basis. There is the medical enquiry and research on those dietary factors which may contribute to morbidity and mortality of men in particular in middle-age, and of both sexes in later life. This includes the general problem of obesity, and the specific problems of angina and coronary artery disease and hardening of the arteries (arteriosclerosis). In under-developed countries, the same enquiry and research is looking at the reverse problem: under-nutrition on a general basis, and specific diseases related to lack of proteins and shortage of vitamins.

There is the interest of public health doctors and pollution-conscious social scientists in the preservatives, additives, colourants and sweeteners added to many foods, and the nutritive constituents removed from them by current methods of processing. This extends back to the fertilising agents, pesticides and growth control agents used in farming today. There is the interest of lay and professional people in the possibility of prolonging life by means of a 'special' diet. Speaking at the Zurich Conference on the Control of Human Ageing in 1971, the gerontologist Dr Alex Comfort reminded his audience of the experiments on rats in which their caloric intake was reduced by almost two-thirds, shortly after birth. The results showed that these rats lived forty per cent longer than rats on regular diets. Dr Comfort was presumably referring to the work of C. M. McCay at Cornell in the United States in the 1930s. The physician, R. McCarrison—later knighted by the British for his work in the India Medical Service—also fed rats on special diets, based this time on tribal eating habits. He found that rats given Sikh and Pathan diets (containing fresh-ground grain and fresh vegetables) had outstandingly better health and resistance to illness than rats fed on

Madrassi or Bengali diets (containing few fresh vegetables and a lot of rice).

In the report of a study of nonagenarians carried out in 1970 by Dr F. Wigzell, a physician in diseases of old age, in the Aberdeen area of Scotland, an important comment was made about the diet of these ninety year olds. Wigzell explained that it was not uncommon for employers of many of these people to have had contractual obligations on diet, in terms of feeding them fresh salmon, venison or game at least once every week. Presumably such a diet was based on the ready availability of these items at low cost in the area. The long-living Caucasians in the Soviet Union enjoy fresh vegetables and fruit, eat at regular times, and are fond of our old friend honey. The accent, then, appears to be on the word 'fresh' rather than on the matter of whether long-living people prefer animal to vegetable food, or cereal to fruit. Fresh—not frozen, fresh—not processed, fresh—not stored, fresh—not highly spiced, fresh—no additives, fresh—no colourants, fresh, natural, unadulterated—this is the message for health and longevity. Or is it?

WHAT DID YOU HAVE FOR DINNER?

The present writer, carrying out a retrospective survey of eating habits and diet in a group of very senior citizens in Lancashire, found several difficulties in obtaining an accurate picture. The power of recall by the old person of 'typical' breakfast, lunch and evening meals at different decades was variable, and often coloured by 'special event' meals like birthdays or Sabbath dinners. Single men had poorer recall than married or widowed men, and women generally had better recall than bachelors or married men. Since the group studied all belonged to the Registrar General's third and fourth social classes, carbohydrate foods often dominated the picture—as chip potatoes, pies (with various fillings), sandwiches (also with various fillings), cereals and flour products. Moreover, those persons studied were all from an industrial community, so the opportunities to obtain—and the economic capacity to purchase—fresh fruit, fresh eggs, fresh vegetables and fresh milk were limited or apparently non-existent. Yet the age range of this group (including both men and women) was 83 to 98 years, with an average figure of 88.9 years. Remembering McCay's experiments with rats, it would have been of considerable interest to obtain the pattern of total daily caloric intake in the infancy of these octogenarians and nonagenarians; but this proved to be an experimental non-starter because of failure of recall.

In the McCay studies of rats on restricted calorie diets, and in the McCarrison studies of rats on Sikh and Pathan diets, the length of survival of the rodents was due to a lessened sensitivity to the diseases and complaints which usually afflict laboratory rodents. McCarrison also noted over a five year period that his rats had a minimal 'maternal mortality' and 'infant mortality'. A more provoking experiment (in socio-political terms) was the report on rats to which McCarrison fed a 'typical working-class diet'—this included boiled potatoes and boiled vegetables, white bread with margarine, and tinned meat products. He found his rats then quickly lost their glossy coat and, over the next five months, contracted the typical lung and bowel complaints of rodents in the laboratory setting.

These rat experiments suggest, at first sight, that it may be possible to put off ageing alterations in the body by adjusting the calories and content of the diet. However, we cannot exclude individual genetic factors in human responses to diet and calories. Experiments on mice of different genetic strains show that varying the quality and quantity of food in the diet may have some effect on longevity in some strains yet none at all in others. We can well conclude that the multifarious human genetic strains, fed on the many and varied diets related to geography, availability, custom, ethnic practice, religious needs and personal fads, may be little influenced by low calorie diets, fresh food intake or special quality control, in terms of prolonged longevity. This does not mean that we should be any less circumspect about food processes which, for instance, destroy vitamins or reduce first-class protein to reach an end-product for consumption. Neither does it mean we should be less vigilant on additives which may increase the risk of tumour production or the chance of mutating genes.

OBESITY

There is no doubt, however, that diets which constantly supply calories in excess of the individual need are likely to shorten the individual life. Any person who seeks to take out life assurance cover and is more than ten to fifteen per cent over ideal weight (for age and height) is likely to have the premium 'loaded'; for actuarial calculations have shown that obesity shortens the expectations of life in men and women. In the middle age group, which we can identify for practical purposes as those between fifty and sixty-five years of age, obesity may reduce the expectation of life by up to twenty-five per cent. The physiologists G. Burrows and A. Everitt, of New South Wales in Australia, have carried out experiments on rats, giving various levels of food intake—including one group of rats allowed to eat food 'ad libitum', that is more than twenty grammes per day. Burrows and Everitt showed that the ageing process in rats measured by changes in tendon collagen and protein excretion was speeded up in those rats permitted unrestricted food intake.

Obesity in humans diminishes longevity in a number of ways. The condition appears to accelerate the 'normal' development of hardening of the arteries, and is also associated with a greater incidence of coronary artery disease and thrombosis in the middle-aged. Again, obesity causes increased wear and tear on weight-bearing joints of the limbs and decreases the stability of older people in walking, climbing and standing—putting them at greater risk from accidents in the home and in the street. Obese people have a higher incidence of chest diseases, especially bronchitis and pneumonia which are always potential killers in older people. Obesity is also associated with raised blood pressures and their secondary effects on the brain and heart.

The life-shortening effects of obesity are more marked in men than in women. In geriatric practice, it is unusual to meet very senior male citizens in the very obese category. Obese women, however, in the very senior age groups, are not uncommonly observed. The heaviest very old lady that the present writer has met was a 91 year old woman living with her daughter and son-in-law in a terraced row in a Lancashire suburb. Her weight was just under 300 pounds (about 135 kilograms) and her daily diet always included a loaf of brown bread, sliced or as sandwiches. She had been over 200 pounds since her twenties, acquiring a significant additional poundage with each pregnancy. Such overweight ladies still suffer from conditions like bronchitis and osteoarthritis, which cause a good deal of chronic illness and morbidity among the over-eighties—but persuading such senior citizens to reduce weight is an invidious task for medical or nursing attendants. Coaxing obese persons of any age group to reduce weight is a hard task—and to maintain weight reduction, often an even harder one. Not surprisingly, the older woman—or man—who has fixed eating habits in terms of both quality and quantity does not take kindly to change, especially when advised to do so by 'youngsters'. Moreover, even if the older person wishes to co-operate in 'a diet', the social and economic circumstances may prevent or limit that co-operation. In Great Britain, for example, the Supplementary Benefits Commission of the Social Security is permitted to pay special monetary allowances to senior citizens on special diets for diabetes or malabsorption disease. If it is 'merely obesity', this is not classified as an illness and no help is forthcoming to replace the carbohydrates, which are cheap, by the first-class proteins, which are expensive.

The top social classes in the Eastern and Western advanced countries enjoy a more varied and calorifically richer diet than the lower social classes, and this continues as a pattern into old age. The pattern may be modified in the post-retiral phase, as Brockington and Lempert in the United Kingdom and Bayne in Canada have shown, by the degree of physical mobility and social interests outside the home as well as by better post-retiral income (with or without a part-time job). Married couples are usually better fed than single persons in very senior years, with single or widowed men much less likely to have a good diet. This last point accounts for the occurrence of scurvy (due to lack of vitamin C) as a subclinical or overt illness in old men living alone, who either cannot cook properly or fail to take fresh fruit, fresh vegetables, tomatoes or fruit juices. (Scurvy is one illness that can certainly be prevented by 'fresh' 'substances.) The British report by the Panel on Nutrition of the Elderly, in 1970, pointed out the difficulties in defining accurately the 'nutritional needs of the elderly'. It did suggest a number of factors which—separately or in combinations—would tend to encourage malnutrition in old people (and thus impair longevity). They included those we have already mentioned, such as social isolation, limited mobility, and lack of interest. Other factors were apathy, ignorance, food fads, lack of income, mental ill-health and carious or absent teeth.

BETTER NUTRITION

In an earlier study, *Later Life*, the present writer suggested an average calorie requirement for the retired elderly man or woman of 2,000 to 2,500 calories a day, with additional levels for those undertaking part-time work or strenuous domestic duties. The Food and Agricultural Organisation (of the World Health Organisation) suggested that the need for energy falls with age, and presumed that the senior citizen's appetite might therefore decrease as the need for energy falls. But in fact, other factors (health, social state, for example) being equal, the appetite may remain much the same, especially in the female old person. In terms of the qualitative constituents of the foods giving calories to the elderly, protein, mineral and vitamin requirements may actually be increased. This is to offset situations where a steady loss may occur—as in post-operative states, and diminished efficiency in digestion or absorption.

It was also pointed out in *Later Life* that up to the mid-seventies, elderly women maintain well-balanced mixed diets including appropriate hot meals, ready-served, and varied cooked foods. In the over-eighties, the balance tends to suffer, especially in those living alone and those in the lower social classes. A 'balanced diet' includes at least one pint of milk (over half a litre) daily, with a good serving of animal protein (meat, cheese, bacon, eggs, fish, liver, kidney) at each of three daily meals—supported by bread, cereal and flour products, vegetables and fruit, and potatoes. The protein, calcium and iron content of this well-balanced diet helps to combat thinning bones and muscles, and to correct iron-deficiency anaemia and diminished resistance to stress and infection. The problems of teeth, or lack of them, in relation to old people's diet and general health will be looked at later. At this point, it is worth noting that good dentition (real teeth or artificial dentures) is no absolute guarantee of a well-balanced food intake in older people.

EDUCATION IN EATING

Three different methods have been adopted to encourage

F

better nutrition and adequate diet in senior citizens. The first is the method of health education—through talks and lectures, at pre-retirement courses or social groups in clubs and societies, through pamphlets and booklets and through television and radio. Secondly, there has been the method of health education combined with practical guidance—through the visits of health visitors and public health nurses, through old people's welfare groups and over-sixties' clubs, and cookery classes for senior citizens. Thirdly, there has been the method of direct practical help—individually from relatives, friends or voluntary workers coming in to cook meals; from pre-cooked meals supplied and delivered at low cost by voluntary or government bodies; or through luncheon clubs or meals at social clubs, with or without individual economic support for the poorer senior citizens. We may add, to these three methods, the general approach of stimulating the appetite of senior citizens by encouraging outside interests apart from dietary ones. Viewers of Lionel Bart's delightful musical *Oliver* will recall the chorus extolling the virtues of 'food, glorious food'. So it should be in later life, too, except that—unlike Oliver Twist—we should not seek second helpings.

ILLNESS AND DIET

Special difficulties arise in ensuring proper nutrition in senior citizens suffering from certain medical problems. The diabetic older person has to limit his intake of sugar and starch foods, because the body's metabolism has difficulty in coping with higher levels of carbohydrate. When diabetes mellitus is newly discovered in over-seventies citizens, it is often very hard to persuade 'new diabetics' to change a pattern of food intake which they have enjoyed for many years. This is apart from the economic problem of a low starch and sugar, high protein diet, which is invariably expensive in the advanced countries and even costlier in the emerging countries. Social security payments in several countries take account of the extra expense of a 'diabetic life' and additional money may be given to permit proper dietary control of the condition.

Another not uncommon alimentary problem in older people is the presence of 'diverticulosis' in the bowels. In this condition, small blind-ended sacs appear at intervals along the main colonic tube of the bowel, and these may go unrecognised and undetected, unless barium X-ray studies are undertaken for any reason. The presence of these sacs or diverticula may be revealed when they collect 'debris' and become infected, causing colicky pain and upset of bowel function, usually diarrhoea. The actual inflammation is treated by antibiotics but there is no 'cure' for the mechanical change in the bowel that produced the sacs. Diet has to be 'controlled', so that food contains a fair amount of bulk to avoid constipation but not an excess of roughage and cellulose to produce 'looseness'. This happy medium of foods can be difficult to achieve in an older person even with good dietary advice from a physician or dietitian, when this is available.

Illnesses like cirrhosis of the liver and failure of kidney function over the years may require careful adjustment of protein intake in older people. This requires supervision by hospital outpatients departments and family physicians, as well as the interest and support of home nurses, public health nurses and relatives and friends. An occasional feature (and problem) in older people suffering from the personality changes due to hardening of brain arteries is the presence of an uninhibited appetite for food. This can result in obesity in an older person who may already be handicapped by other arterial problems. Psychiatric help and drug control may be required. Sometimes, whatever physical or mental illness is present, the attendants on a very senior citizen are obliged to provide 'just what that citizen likes' in order to ensure that something is eaten. For example, in the programme

'Blue Peter', televised for children on the British Broadcasting Corporation network, an old lady of 107 years was interviewed in early February 1972. Deaf, frail, white-haired but cheerful, this grand centenarian was asked by the interviewer what she most liked at mealtimes. The answer was firm and forceful: 'Why, Cornish pasties, of course!' It would have been pointless to offer that charming lady a fillet steak and French fried potatoes as a balanced meal. She would have what she liked....

CHAPTER 8

'Boosters' and 'Tonics'

VITAMINS ARE VITAL

AN EXPATRIATE SCOTTISH SOLDIER, ALEXANDER MACDONALD, lived the greater part of his life in France. He died in Fontainebleau in the year 1784 and the records suggest his age was in the region of 110 years. Macdonald had served in the ill-fated Scottish rebellion of 1715 and escaped to France the same year. The records state that 'he lived entirely on vegetables' for the last ten years of his life, and he 'enjoyed a good state of health until a few days before he died'. Mrs Mary Rogers, a well-known resident of Penzance in Cornwall, England, also eschewed animal foods in the last part of her life. She died in the year 1779 and was also reputed to have an age approaching 110 years. In her middle age and old age, the records tell us, 'she lived exclusively on vegetables'. John Yarrow of Crookham in England was a farmer all his days in the north-east of the country and he, too, allegedly reached his 110 years mark. Like Macdonald and Rogers, the records claim that his diet contained a 'very small proportion of animal food'.

Despite these examples of the possible efficacy of vegetables in helping senior citizens to reach centenarian years, an early nineteenth century author in a 'code of health' manuscript advised that 'aged people' ought 'generally to use vegetables very sparingly' or even to cut them out altogether. The well-meaning author does not indicate to us why he has such antipathy to vegetables for older people. We may surmise, however, that even in those days of lesser scientific observation, the effect of much vegetable 'bulk' or residue after digestion was noted. That effect is to loosen the bowel motion generally, and to provoke actual diarrhoea in sufferers from bowel muscular changes (diverticulosis) or inflammation (colitis). Bowel function apart, the suggestion of avoiding vegetables is even more curious when one realises that James Lind and Gilbert Blane, physicians in the English Navy in the late 1700s, had already shown the efficacy of vegetables (and fresh fruit and lemon juice) in preventing scurvy in seamen on long cruises.

Not until 1912, however, was the idea put forward of 'accessory factors in food' as substances which might prevent the development of certain illnesses, such as scurvy, rickets and beri-beri. The concept of an essential factor that is present in certain foods in tiny quantities—and causes disease if it is lacking in the diet—is attributed to C. Funk, who experimented on beri-beri prevention in birds at the Lister Institute in England. He succeeded in his experiments in 1912, using extracts from rice polishings. The name coined for each of these essential factors, 'vitamin', is said to have been derived from the twin notions—'life supporting' hence vita, and 'protein derived' hence amine. Even though later work showed these essential factors are not amines, the name 'vitamin' held fast. By 1932, the vitamins labelled A, D, E and C, and several of the B group, had been identified and isolated; vitamin K was added to the list in 1939. Not until 1948, however, was the anti-pernicious anaemia product, vitamin B12, produced in purified form by scientists in the United Kingdom and in the United States almost simultaneously. Today, the role of each vitamin in the cellular and biochemical activity of the human body is known, and the daily quantity required to maintain health at different ages has also been assessed.

DEFICIENCY AND DISEASE

It was mentioned in the last chapter that older people living alone on a fixed income, particularly bachelors or widowers, may be at risk through failure to provide themselves with an adequate and balanced diet particularly where vitamins are concerned. Lack of vitamin C (ascorbic acid) may lead to signs of scurvy, where fresh fruit and fresh vegetables are infrequently or rarely taken. Some years ago, the Food and Nutrition Board of the National Research Council in the United States suggested an intake of at least 60 milligrams of vitamin C each day as the requirement for a senior citizen. These recommendations were published in 1968, but fourteen years earlier the Committee on Nutrition of the British Medical Association had suggested a much lower figure, around 30 milligrams daily, as a 'safety intake'. Surveys like those of M. Brin in the United States and M. Kataria in Great Britain have shown that senior citizens in 'institutional' settings—hospitals, hostels, old people's homes, extended care facilities—may be at greater risk from low intake of vitamin C than in their own homes. J. Andrews and co-workers have shown that this risk is greater in winter months.

Although diseases due to deficiency of vitamins may—like any illness—help to accelerate the ageing process in various tissues, no one vitamin has any known anti-ageing property by itself. Older people suffering from vague symptoms such as 'being below par' or 'lacking pep' may self-medicate with a multiple vitamin preparation. However, if the diet is a healthy, normal one and the body's vitamin stores are adequate, then the only real gain is a psychological one (apart from the gain to the vitamin salesman). No beneficial effect comes from excessive body stores—and in the case of excess vitamin D, actual harmful effects in senior citizens, including the depositing of calcium material in the kidneys, are well recognised. Vitamin A excess, too, can produce toxic effects such as loss of hair, anaemia and skin changes. (This contrasts with the effects of larger doses of vitamin A in the experimental animal. According to J. Freeman, for example, extra vitamin A in such animals does lengthen male and female lives and also prolongs the reproductive time span.)

Vitamin B12, a deficiency of which causes pernicious anaemia, can be given by injection to patients suffering from the anaemia illness. Such patients are not 'cured' but the complaint is kept under control and the blood picture returns to normal (provided therapy with B12 is continued for life). Lack of this vitamin can produce changes in nerve cells, usually of the spinal cord, leading to weakness of muscles and loss of feeling in the limbs. The brain cells are sometimes affected, resulting in the deterioration of intellect, emotion and memory known as dementia. B12 deficiency occurs in middle age and later life, as a general rule. Studies such as those of D. Dawson and A. Donald in Scotland, and B. Chow in the United States, have shown a fall in the storage level of B12 in older people's blood over the years, even in the absence of pernicious anaemia. R. Strachan and J. Henderson have suggested that some mental changes in senior citizens may be due to low vitamin B12 levels, before the pernicious anaemia fully develops. The logical steps are, firstly, to screen all patients developing dementia to determine the possibility of vitamin B12 deficiency, and secondly, to treat patients with a low B12 level in the blood, and dementia (but no evidence of pernicious anaemia), with injections of B12. Unhappily, even in dementia in the presence of proven B12 deficiency and pernicious anaemia, reversal of the mental changes with treatment is generally limited. During treatment by the author of a series of fourteen patients over the age of seventy, all with proven pernicious anaemia and signs of dementia, only one showed almost complete recovery of her mental state. This was a woman of 82 years, who lived in a country village with her daughter and their family. She had an eighteen months' history of mental change. Eventually she was discharged on therapy back to the daughter's home, but the dementia reappeared five months later.

Vitamin B12 thus has no anti-ageing power on the human brain. It is sometimes prescribed as a 'tonic' or 'booster' in vague complaints of weakness and apathy and tiredness in older persons, but this is a potentially dangerous 'tonic' in the sense that a 'one-shot course' of therapy could mask an underlying pernicious anaemia. B12 would be given only for a short time and a proper diagnosis would be postponed, in the meantime risking possible spinal cord nerve changes through failure to continue therapy for life.

Perhaps the most controversial vitamin is alpha-tocopherol or vitamin E. It is sometimes known as the 'anti-sterility' vitamin because the original discovery was based on a deficiency in rats' diet which made the rats sterile. Wheat germ oil is the best source of alpha-tocopherol in its natural form. In animals, vitamin E plays a part in the healthy function of muscles, as well as in reproductive function; but although it has been tried as therapy in both infertility and muscular dystrophy in human beings, no real value has ever been proved conclusively. Orthodox medical opinion does not recognise any marked signs of vitamin E deficiency in human beings. There is no evidence that it can act against impotence, or work generally as an aphrodisiac, as has been claimed.

In the body tissues, vitamin E is a powerful anti-oxidant, particularly effective against the oxidation of unsaturated fatty acids (like linoleic acid). Therefore some workers have suggested that in diets containing large quantities of vegetable oils, used to help protect against the development of atheroma in arteries, additional vitamin E should be prescribed. The Canadian cardiologist, W. Shute, has long advocated high doses in the treatment of coronary artery disease, but few other specialists consider this a part of standard therapy in human heart disease. The anti-ageing role of vitamin E, in terms of prevention or protection against arterial disease, is still undecided. Meanwhile, health food establishments in a number of countries promote alpha-tocopherol in natural and tablet presentation for 'better health'. At least, its promotion as an aphrodisiac has now all but disappeared.

The vitamin B group of chemical substances can individually cause a number of deficiency complaints, such as pellagra and beri-beri. In elderly persons, deficiency of B vitamins is generally part of an overall lack of vitamins and proper diet. We have already noted such 'at risk' persons as those living alone, the disabled or poorly mobile, and those not visited regularly or on a fixed income. To these may be added the mentally disturbed and the mentally backward, as well as the food faddists. Vitamin B deficiency is of particular significance in the alcoholic who frequently fails to eat a normal diet. Changes which occur in the memory and personality of the alcoholic may be improved and reversed by withdrawal of alcohol and administration of large doses of vitamin B group by injection. This is true at any age, but reversal of dementia changes is less satisfactory in the elderly alcoholic.

BLEEDING AND ANAEMIA

The importance of arteriosclerosis and atheroma as factors which pathologically accelerate the ageing processes has been stressed at several points in this book. The narrowed, tortuous and inelastic arteries fail to deliver adequate supplies of blood to the organs and tissues in need. Even if arteriosclerosis and atheroma are minimal in elderly citizens, so that the volume of blood is satisfactory, the quality of the blood being circulated and supplied may be suspect. This is not to imply that the sometime popular notion that the blood becomes 'thinner' with ageing is in any way true. The thickness of the blood— that is, the number of red cells and their individual content of haemoglobin (the red pigment to which the oxygen is attached)—can remain at the same levels in very senior citizens as in young adults, other factors being equal. However, a number of possibilities occur in the elderly person which may act separately or collectively to produce the commonest form of anaemia in old age, namely iron deficiency anaemia. Lack of iron leads to lack of haemoglobin (which contains elemental iron in its molecule) and this in turn diminishes the oxygen supply, encouraging or speeding up ageing of organs and tissues as the months and years advance.

Many international studies are available which confirm the presence of mild or moderate iron deficiency anaemia in the elderly, both in general populations and in sheltered or special accommodation populations. For example, H. Katsunuma and co-workers in Tokyo examined 1,000 older people in that city to assess the presence of anaemia. They found blood haemoglobin levels varying between 52 per cent of normal and 80 per cent of normal. Similarly, L. Hallberg in a Swedish study of 71 women over the age of 75 years, in Gothenburg, found a prevalence of anaemia (haemoglobin below 80 per cent of normal) in 23 per cent of the women. In 60 per cent of those, the prime cause was lack of iron. T. Mitchell and G. Pegrum in their London study of a routine hospital admission group of 49 patients—age range 70 to 90 years—found anaemia in 22 of those studied. Again the haemoglobin levels varied between 80 per cent (often used as the 'dividing point' below which anaemia is considered to be present) and 50 per cent. In all the studies, the frequency of iron deficiency anaemia is very much greater in women than in men.

Iron deficiency anaemia is also the commonest cause of a low haemoglobin level in young women up to the menopause. Between 13 and 50 years, the lack of iron results physiologically from blood loss at regular menstruation, from the developing baby's use of the mother's 'iron stores' in pregnancy and from relative lack of iron in the diet. There may be additional pathological causes, such as chronic bleeding from an ulcer in the stomach or from haemorrhoids. (In younger men, iron deficiency anaemia is invariably due to a pathological loss of blood.)

At one time, the frequency of iron deficiency anaemia in older women was attributed to an ongoing anaemia from before the menopause, plus a relative or absolute lack of iron in the diet of the senior lady citizen. More recent studies, such as the Swedish study by L. Hallberg or the British study by D. Evans and M. Pathy, confirm the current view, that blood loss in the immediate past or earlier is the most frequent cause of iron deficiency anaemia in elderly men and women. Lack of iron-containing foods in the diet—insufficient meat, eggs and green vegetables—may contribute to already lowered iron stores in the blood and accentuate the anaemia from blood loss. We also know that ageing changes in the stomach lining, which reduce the stomach's output of hydrochloric acid, decrease the body's ability to absorb iron from foodstuff. In therapy, this can be countered by giving iron by injection, either into the muscle or directly into a vein, instead of as 'the tablet'. In H. Katsunuma's Tokyo study in Japan, it was further suggested that the blood supply from the bone marrow—where new red blood cells are constantly manufactured to replace the old ones—is depleted by the familiar enemy of age, arteriosclerosis. The arteries supplying the marrow nutrition themselves become narrow and hardened, and fail to function effectively.

The effects of mild iron deficiency may be unspectacular, but can account for chronic vague ill-health and lassitude in older people. In severe forms, it produces breathlessness, weakness, confusion, cardiac disorder and changes in nails, skin and gullet. In the over-eighties such changes, whether minor or more marked, may be mistakenly ascribed to 'ageing' when they are in fact due to a readily correctable cause, iron deficiency. The underlying cause of blood loss may also be amenable to treatment, as in the case of ulcers or piles.

EAT MORE IRON

One of the important activities in preventive health clinics for middle-aged and older citizens is checking the blood count and haemoglobin, a fairly simple procedure which does not inconvenience the examinee very much. In the pioneer Rutherglen clinic in Scotland, established by W. F. Anderson and N. Cowan in 1952, patients over 55 years were referred through or by the family physician, and various blood tests and clinical measurements were made. These tests were carried out in the healthy as well as the less healthy. Again, in the test results, women were more often anaemic than men in the seventies age group, but the actual degree of anaemia was much lower than expected. Out of 500 ambulant old people who attended the preventive clinic over a two year period, nearly 400 had a haemoglobin level of 80 per cent or over. Those who were found to be anaemic were treated with iron and investigated further where there were indications of a cause other than a simple lack of iron-containing food in the diet. Ensuring the maintenance of a healthy blood count and haemoglobin is thus an example of 'retarding' ageing processes by attention to health in middle age. In more senior years, periodic screening surveys of 'local populations', such as the family physician survey undertaken by I. Williams in Bolton, England, reveal the mild anaemia that can be corrected by iron therapy and a better diet. In his survey of 350 patients over the age of 75, for example, Williams discovered 20 old people who were clearly receiving insufficient food each day—insufficient, that is, in terms of the minimum intake of protein, fat, carbohydrate, vitamins and minerals advised by the various national nutrition bodies and the Food and Agricultural Organisation of the World Health Organisation.

The intake of dietary iron required to maintain 'iron balance' and avoid iron deficiency anaemia has been variously estimated in Canada, the United Kingdom, Australia and the United States as between 10 and 20 milligrams per day. Hallberg's Swedish study, mentioned earlier, showed an average daily intake of iron per day, in the 75 years age group of women, as only 7.9 milligrams. Almost a third of these women had an actual iron intake of below 7 milligrams. In the study, the low iron intake was due not so much to a diet low in sources of iron, but rather to a greatly diminished intake of total quantities of the iron-containing foods. Unless older people can be persuaded to eat larger quantities of iron-containing foods—and this may be precluded for economic reasons, or through lack of appetite or interest—periodic iron supplements will be necessary. Some older people self-medicate with iron-containing 'tonics' and unwittingly compensate for a low iron intake in food. R. Macdonald, in a 1964 study, pointed out that alcohol intake may affect iron stores. For example, a litre bottle of a popular French wine may contain up to 6 milligrams of iron, and a similar sized bottle of domestic wine in the United States or Britain may contain from 2 to 5 milligrams of iron. Beer and spirits have a low iron content, however, so the elderly person who wishes to avoid anaemia through alcohol must be selective, it seems.

CHAPTER 9

Well, Tap and Bottle

DON'T DRY UP

LEWIS MORGAN OF WALES WAS A CENTENARIAN WHO, LIKE MAC-
donald, Yarrow and Rogers mentioned in the last chapter,
lived on a diet consisting chiefly of vegetables. He reached the
age of 101 years before dying, in 1785, as the result of a fall.
Where Morgan differs from the others is that his beverage was
non-alcoholic: he eschewed all but spring water.

Water is an essential nutrient for all forms of life and
physiologists are fond of pointing out that in an adult man,
60 per cent of weight is water while in an adult woman 50 per
cent of weight is water. This fact presumably puts the rest of
the body constituents in proper proportion. It emphasises the
significance of water as an important part of human cells and
tissues—and this is true no less in the elderly body than in
that of the infant or young adult. The daily intake of water—
both as water itself and as part of food and beverages—helps
to ensure a free flow of urine from the kidneys, with the consequent excretion of toxic and waste products extracted from
the bloodstream. Healthy kidneys need to put out at least 700
millilitres of urine in a twenty-four hour period, to clear such
waste products. If we add to this the fluid lost through sweating and invisible perspiration, as well as the moisture of
exhaled air, we can reckon a suitable minimum intake of
water to match the output as around two litres per day.

People whose kidneys are diseased due to changes from

infection or inflammation, or the presence of a stone, require a much greater intake of fluid to ensure satisfactory clearance of waste products from the bloodstream. Hardening of the arteries in senior citizens can affect the arteries of the kidneys as well as other organs, without any immediately obvious 'kidney complaint' or 'attack'. Any lowering of fluid intake in an older person may therefore interfere with elimination of urea and other waste products, and produce a decline in health.

Some old people have a tendency to reduce their water intake, either because they imagine they need less or because they are having difficulty in controlling urine function. The latter condition may result from local infection of the bladder, or a gynaecological condition like prolapse, or occur as part of disease of the brain and nervous system. Because of the possible kidney changes in old people, however, a much greater intake of fluid is recommended—at least three litres each day. Unsuspected dehydration and untreated water lack can certainly accelerate illness of any other kind and may encourage a breakdown in the health of any senior citizen, however well previously. The alert physician of the elderly is always on the look-out for such tell-tale signs as a dry tongue, dry skin, increased wrinkling and decreased elasticity of the skin lining, sunken eye appearance or the more serious features associated with a rising blood urea. The simple measure of encouraging water intake—as tea, coffee, juices, cordials, or plain water— in plentiful amounts, whether the older person is at home or in hospital, often produces a 'surprising' improvement in the patient's condition. It is one of the measures which may convert the state of being muddled and confused into a state of reasonable lucidity for an old person.

In Chapter 4 we considered the matter of the dissolved solids and elements in drinking water. In particular, we noted the evidence of some investigations that people whose drinking water is 'hard'—that is, contains large amounts of dissolved

WELL, TAP AND BOTTLE

minerals—run less risk of hardening of the arteries than people whose drinking water is 'soft'. Bailey, a student of health and longevity in the early nineteenth century, pointed out that the favourite of centenarians, spring water, is purer than pump or well water and is likely to contain less 'insoluble carbonate or sulphate of lime'. However, it will depend on whether the spring flows through a more or less limestone-containing area. Anticipating, perhaps, the current views of scientists in medicine on water and health, Bailey declared that hard water is a superior drink for healthy persons—and soft water is 'suited for dyspeptical persons and for culinary and pharmaceutical processes'.

WATER AND TEETH

Another useful constituent of water, that Bailey did not know about, is fluoride. Generally present as the dissolved salt, calcium fluoride or sodium fluoride, this element has been shown to protect teeth against decay where the fluoride level is around one part per million. The World Health Organisation has advised that in those countries and areas where natural fluoridation is absent, 'controlled fluoridation of drinking water is a practicable and effective public health measure'. Strong, healthy, natural teeth not only contribute to the maintenance of a youthful appearance, but also permit a more varied and nutritious diet for the older person who can bite and chew and masticate so much more effectively and pleasurably. Thanks to the fluoridation of water in the pro-grammes of such countries as Australia, Canada, New Zealand, the United Kingdom and the United States, future senior citizens may have much better dentition than contemporary old people. This should help to contribute to better general health. Apart from the fluoride question, water is of import-ance in general mouth hygiene. This includes its use in 'foaming' toothpaste for teeth cleansing and as the basic in-

G

gredient of mouth rinses, mouthwashes, gargles and preparations for cleaning dentures. Cleansing the mouth and teeth of food debris, unwanted bacteria and undesirable fungus helps the nutrition and diet and digestion at all ages but particularly in senior citizens.

B. Hedegard has shown that older people in 'institutional situations' run a greater risk of poor oral hygiene, and has recommended increased attention to oral hygiene and dental care in hostels, old people's homes, geriatric hospital departments and extended care facilities. His Swedish study again underlines the value of detecting older people 'at risk' to various forms of ill-health and disability—and also the value of plentiful water intake. He has also pointed out—in what are known as 'mouth stereognosis' studies—that the sensitivity of the older mouth as a 'tasting structure' is decreased by the absence of natural teeth. This lessened sensitivity can also be achieved experimentally by artificially coating normal teeth with wax. The implication is that dry, unwashed, debris-laden teeth will also have reduced sensitivity in recognising the tasted or chewed object, and so limit one of the senior citizen's pleasures—a well-recognised, well-enjoyed meal. (Mouth stereognosis studies in older people may also be a useful factor in helping to choose those older people who will cope more easily with artificial dentures, when supplied for either functional or aesthetic purposes.)

DRINK, DRANK, DRUNK

The recommendation of a liquid intake of at least three litres a day for older people does not, of course, imply that an unlimited self-indulgence in the pleasures of alcohol is in any way beneficial. Alcoholism can be regarded as an addiction, comparable with drug dependence and having similar antisocial consequences. Regular excessive consumption of alcohol, as beer, wines and spirits, or derived from other sources, leads to mental changes, as we noted during our discussion on vitamins, and also to physical changes, including weight loss, gastritis and cirrhosis of the liver. In older people, the liver may be less capable of coping with potentially poisonous substances ingested by the individual. This applies to drugs and to alcohol. Therefore relatively low levels of alcoholic intake in a senior citizen who regards his consumption as 'moderate' may still affect the body adversely. D. Kay of England has pointed out how 'chronic alcoholism' can markedly affect the older person's reactions in the presence of brain changes due to hardening of the arteries.

G. Salzberger of New York has made a special study of alcoholism in senior citizens. Since confusion is the commonest presenting symptom of any illness in old people, not surprisingly a confused state is common in elderly alcoholics. Treatment includes arranging a suitable 'therapeutic environment' (that is, temporary removal from the normal stressful milieu), providing an adequate diet including vitamin B supplements, withdrawing all alcohol, and prescribing suitable tranquillisers. Aversion therapy using drugs may be less satisfactory than the psychological value of 'group therapy'. The patient's lowered resistance to infection also calls for prophylaxis for example against pneumonia—by giving antibiotics like penicillin.

Such findings might suggest the advisability of a medical ban on alcohol intake in old age, as a recommendation, if not as a firm prohibition, even in otherwise healthy senior citizens; but the chances of success for such a ban can be judged by the popularity of 'social drinking' among the elders of the community in many countries. An elderly Frenchman enjoying the pleasures of good wine would be just as contemptuous of such a ban as his opposite number enjoying draught beer in an English public house. Moreover, retrospective medical studies do not give much factual ammunition to the argument that temperance is a major guarantee of longevity. J. McHugh and R. Taylor's study of thirty-two patients who had died in their hundredth year did not show any direct relationship between regular drinking habits and the eventual cause of death. A similar study by T. Howell of nearly 400 octogenarians showed only one fatality directly attributable to cirrhosis of the liver. (Admittedly, however, senior citizens invariably show evidence of many pathological changes which can all contribute to demise, even though only one specific condition acts as the final agent.) Of the thirty-four Hungarian centenarians studied by G. Acsadi and A. Klinger, one third were said to have been 'regular drinkers' and eight were 'habitual drinkers'. Of the latter, five were still enjoying regular alcohol. Half of the entire group had been intermittent social partakers of alcohol. In the present writer's group of six centenarians, all had consumed alcohol at times on a social basis.

A famous eighteenth century example of a man who departed from 'all those rules of temperance and exercise which so much influence longevity' (to quote a biographer of the period) was William Davies, Rector of Staunton-upon-Wye in England. He died, reputedly aged 105 years, in the year 1790, and during the last thirty-five years of his life 'never used any exercise' apart from pottering about his home, and always ate well and 'drank wine' though not to great excess. Similarly, Anne Davis of Gloucestershire in England, Onassio Gabriello of Messina in Italy, and Anna Loveken of Hanover in Germany, were all eighteenth century centenarians who reputedly eschewed exercise and temperance.

The use by elderly people of alcohol—generally sherry, wine, whisky or brandy—in small amounts, as a 'nightcap' or a sedative at bedtime, is well recognised by physicians attending senior citizens. Doctors are unlikely to discourage such a practice unless it clearly affects mental function during the night or the following day, or interferes with other medication being prescribed, or with normal diet.

A NOTE ON RADIATION

Our discussions so far have concentrated on the structure and function of those parts of the human body where changes that are the result of ageing can be detected and identified; and the emphasis has been on factors of health, environment and nutrition which can to some extent be influenced by the choices and actions of the individual—helped, where necessary, by specialist advice and medical treatment. There remains, however, one important environmental factor, about which there is limited positive knowledge of its effects on the human body, its role in the ageing process, or possible measures to counteract these. Before we go on to consider the social implications of ageing in the chapters that follow, we should mention, at least in passing, the problem of the invisible ion.

Thanks to the mass media, there are few children or adults nowadays who are not aware of the power and presence of radiation, in one form or another, as part of daily life. Radiation has the effect of dislodging electrons from the atom, and producing ions. That ionisation, in which the atom changes its chemical properties, having been given a temporary electric charge, is produced by gamma rays, X-rays and the (perhaps less familiar) alpha and beta rays. There are also cosmic rays, produced by the sun and in outer space—and the protons and mesons, too, are part of ionising radiation today. Such radiations, for example from X-ray apparatus, or nuclear reactors, or therapeutic isotopes, can be measured with suitable Geiger or scintillation counters or 'exposure' film gauges. All forms of ionising radiation are capable of interfering with the function and health of living tissue, human and animal. In particular, ionisation affects the cell protein concerned with 'reprinting' important chemical factors, called enzymes. Actively dividing cells are more prone to damage by ionising radiation (more radio-sensitive), and this is the basic principle of treatment of malignant tissue, many forms of which show very active division processes. Unfortunately, healthy tissues also have active division, such as the bone marrow manufacturing blood, and the gonads manufacturing new sperm and ova. Hence ionising radiation can produce severe anaemia and lack of white cells, and may also affect the genes in the gonad material—the alteration called mutation.

Experiments with ionising radiation, for example on rats by V. Milko of the Soviet Union, and on mice by P. Lindop and J. Rotblat in London, have established certain effects of radiation on the life span of these experimental animals and on changes in their organs and tissues. Milko's experiments on rats, using irradiation with radioactive isotopes, showed that the two important hormonal glands—the thyroid and the adrenals—have reduced output and function. This is more evident in older rats than in younger adult rats. We may infer that the ageing process in hormonal glands, which may already have begun in the older rats (though we do not know the exact nature of this 'ageing'), is speeded up by radiation. Lindop and Rotblat compared mice exposed to irradiation with 'control' mice, and noted similarly that 'old age changes' occurred sooner than expected in the irradiated mice. In any radiation effect, the quantity of radiation applied and the rate at which that quantity is given determine the results: burns, normal tissue change to malignancy, mutation, death or acceleration of natural degeneration processes. A. Comfort had pointed out how difficult it is to judge whether small doses of radiation—to which most people are exposed at some time in their lives today (from X-rays, cosmic rays, radioactive 'fall-out')—genuinely shorten human life. Larger doses certainly do so, by causing leukaemia, blood changes, and cancerous changes in the body. Hence, the elaborate controls and protection methods applied in the industrial, medical, and commercial fields as well as in the experimental use of radiation sources and radioactive materials. It may be that radiation in small doses is just one more factor, of the many we have discussed in these pages, which create the sum total of 'ageing factors' that affect cells, organs and the whole human body, given sufficient time.

On the other hand, irradiation in small doses, over a period of time, may be the key to the damage to the DNA molecule in the cell (as in the ageing theory described in Chapter 3), and its tie-up with ribonucleic acid and enzymes in 'cellular information and replication processes'. If so, we could help to slow up ageing by reducing even small dosage irradiation to a minimum. To this could be added methods of screening and protecting individuals likely to be so exposed (for example, by finding and routinely administering an 'anti-radiation effect' vaccine) or by developing chemicals which reverse specific radiation effects. Then perhaps the ion will no longer be Shelley's 'white radiance of eternity' but more like Arthur Stanley's 'glimpse of the hope of immortality'.

CHAPTER 10

Work, the Grand Cure

OCCUPATION AND LONGEVITY

EASTON, A DISTINGUISHED OBSERVER OF OLD AGE IN ENGLAND
in the early nineteenth century, advised his readers that 'it is
not the rich and the great, or those who depend on medicine
or a special diet, who reach old age'. In fact, he explains, it is
those who 'use much exercise, are exposed to fresh air and
whose food is plain and moderate' that reach very senior years.
He singles out certain occupations which appear to be associated with considerable longevity, and names these as 'farmers,
gardeners, fishermen, labourers and soldiers'. Such occupations do invariably call for considerable muscular activity,
often in an open-air setting. On the other hand, the last three
are not particularly associated with eating 'plain' food in
'moderate' quantities. Neither are any of the five occupations
mentioned commonly associated with 'absolute temperance'
or non-drinking of alcoholic beverages—a requirement for
reaching advanced years which a contemporary of Easton's, a
Doctor Percy of Birmingham, England, insisted upon.

The occupations which Easton singled out are generally
assumed to be male in character and are certainly male-
dominated in Europe and the Americas but not specifically so
in Soviet Russia, Eastern Europe and major parts of Asia and
the Far East. Yet we know from current statistics in most
countries of the world that the expectation of life at birth by
women exceeds that for men by at least four years—and that

there are many more women than men in the eighties, nineties and hundreds. Dr F. Wigzell, in his 1970 study of nonagenarians in the Aberdeen area of Scotland, reported that
many of the female ninety year olds had left school before
their mid-teens and had worked in light, indoor occupations,
such as domestic service, seamstress, governess, housekeeper,
cook and 'table maid'. The oldest patient in the present
writer's hospital practice is a spinster, Miss E.K., who is in her
one hundred and fourth year at the time of writing. She
started work as an apprentice dressmaker at the age of thirteen, and her favourite pastime as a young woman was walking in the countryside. Another hospitalised lady centenarian,
a widow, Mrs J.B., began work 'in service' at the age of twelve
but was 'married off' to a farmer and after that worked in 'the
open air' all her days.

On the other hand, among the long-lived peasants in the
Caucasus, whom we mentioned in the first chapter, women
help with the poultry and take part in the animal husbandry
as well as undertaking household duties and joining in the
collective farming programmes.

A separate study of 'occupation and longevity', undertaken
for the British journal *History of Medicine* in 1970, by the
present writer, looked at the jobs of centenarians in England
and the United States in the eighteenth and early ninetcenth
centuries. The pattern of occupations in these very senior
citizens was very varied and often, as might be expected,
simply reflected both the kind of work available to women as
women, and the kind of work available in the geographic
location. Among the occupations of this kind were sewing,
spinning, knitting, weaving and netmaking. The occurrence
of surnames with job connotations was noteworthy—ladies by
the delightful names of Brown, White, Rose, Speed, Holme,
and Knott, for example, with exceptions like Haynes and
Spicer, however. The last two were remarkable centenarian
widows—Sara Haynes had twelve children and continued to

support herself after widowhood without recourse to her family by the making and selling of high-quality hose, knitted in her own home, until her vision began to fail. This was in her ninth decade and she went on to reach one hundred and three years, whereas Eleanora Spicer, an American lady of the same vintage, continued her spinning activities until six months before her death.

Another interesting group of centenarians were those with the 'occupation' of mistress (rather than legal housewife, that is). Names from an international list of such ladies included Pettit, Freiberg, Rudd, Valker, Yates, Mackenzie and Gillet. Peggy Gillet was a hardy and plucky Scots lady, from the north-east of that rugged land. She was the mistress of two soldiers in the eighteenth century who died—one after the other—before she finally married legally a third soldier, Tom Gillet, and produced a fine large family. Hyacinth Rosa Mackenzie, of mixed blood, mainly Spanish, was one of those ladies who married to ensure respectability but whose 'romantic nature' led her far afield in the English counties. Reaching her hundredth year in 1820, she was taken ill in the same year while 'entertaining' some acquaintances at a party.

Neither social anthropologists nor census directors, who are purists about occupations, are likely to accept 'mistress (courtesan type)' as a bona fide career. A point worth considering, however, is that ladies of this kind were at high risk from a number of diseases—venereal especially—yet attained a remarkable longevity. Since they were neither in 'light work, open air work or in work with general muscular exercise', the longevity figures suggest that factors other than occupation are significant. Just being feminine for one thing, and presumably being well-fed for another, must have contributed to advanced old age, leaving aside genetics and heredity.

An ironical comparison, in the same study, was the frequency of nursing midwives who reached very senior years. A remarkable example was Mrs Rachel Huddie, who reached her centenary birthday in the last decade of the eighteenth century. A stout English woman from Somerset became blind due to cataracts in both eyes. She remained active, however, and combined an increased sensitivity of touch with a powerful reputation. This permitted her to continue the practice of midwifery until a few months before her death.

In more modern times, an interesting Danish study known as the 'Samso Project' was reported by J. Nielsen of the Demographic-Genetic Research Unit in Risskov. Samso is a popular tourist-frequented island in the Kattegat, with a population that was over seven thousand at the turn of this century but had decreased to six thousand by 1961. Essentially rural in character, the island has been losing its youngsters steadily to Denmark's cities. Nielsen noted that the population was otherwise stable with only a third of the people born outside the island. Farming was the main source of income for over fifty per cent of the men, with twenty per cent in commerce and a small per cent only in fishing or unskilled jobs. A significant feature was that 'very few of the married women work outside their homes'. Doctor Nielsen was in fact concerned with psychiatric problems and services in this well-circumscribed rural community. From the aspect of our present discussion of occupation and longevity, however, his report co-incidentally revealed that there were fewer men than women over the age of eighty-five years (which is what we have come to expect from other findings) and that most of the women reaching very senior years were 'non-working' housewives. Admittedly the activity rate (as a fair generalisation) of 'non-working' housewives in rural districts is greater than their counterparts in urban areas; at least, it was in the days when women in cities rarely combined a career as a housewife with a career of a professional or clerical type. Still, the Samso picture is a strong hint that the relationship between work and reaching advanced years does not, for women at any rate, lie in the job itself.

CLASSIFYING WORK

A truly international comparison of occupation and longevity based on accurate figures of jobs actually done and personal or unit survival cannot yet be properly undertaken. It is a mere fourteen years since the International Standard Classification of Occupations was first published and a mere eight years since the *United Nations Demographic Yearbook* produced a simpler classification of eleven basic groups. This includes a group called 'members of the armed forces' and another group called 'workers not classifiable by occupation' as well as more obvious groups like 'craftsmen', 'professional and technical', 'transport and communication', and 'miners and quarrymen', for example. M. Derruau, in his 1961 study of human geography, pointed out that the social structure gives a useful picture of society—one that may help us more than individual occupation in assessing reasons for longevity. For example, in West Germany there is a high proportion of rural people who are not farmers, whereas in parts of France (like the Languedoc) there are many farm workers. Again in Australia, there are large numbers employed in commerce and in trading but there are also small rural groups with high living standards. South Africa and North Africa show contrasting living standards and differences in rural structures and social dependence.

In Great Britain, the tie-up of occupation, living standards and so-called social class is made in the Registrar General's classifications. These are 1. Professional, 2. Intermediate, 3. Skilled, 4. Partly skilled, and 5. Unskilled. (Roman numerals are used in official reports rather than Arab numerals.) A number of British studies using this classification have shown the advantages in the first two classes, in terms of survival past eighty years, over the fourth and fifth classes. For example in the Stockport survey in north-west England, published in 1966, F. Brockington and S. M. Lempert showed that after the eightieth year, the fourth and fifth social classes had statistically significant higher death rates than the first and second classes. Similar conclusions can be drawn from the Bolton, England, survey by Dr E. I. Williams in 1971 and the Glasgow survey by Dr B. Isaacs in 1972.

WORKING CONDITIONS

The relationship between occupation and longevity can also be looked at in terms of jobs which appear likely to shorten the individual life. In the industrial societies of the United States and Europe, for example, many of the factory processes and mining and quarrying procedures led to the widespread presence of chest diseases—from the simpler but often ultimately crippling chronic bronchitis (known as 'the English disease') to the more complex but often equally crippling silicosis, pneumoconiosis and byssinosis. The effects of these dust diseases were firstly to produce shortness of breath, which was progressive and led secondly to resignation from employment or the transfer of the sufferer to 'lighter' work. In time, secondary to the chest disease, the heart became strained and eventually went into failure resulting in death in middle age. Admittedly there has been steady improvement in the working conditions in these previously very dusty environments, with the introduction of better ventilation, air extraction and purifying, protective masks and spraying and wetting processes. The industrial health regulations in different countries provide for radiological and clinical checks on the chest condition of workers at risk. Even so, chronic bronchitis and occupational chest diseases still account for a population mortality of around eight per cent in the over-fifties in the United Kingdom. The other side of the work coin is that sedentary workers—in professions, trade and commerce—who are exposed to fewer environmental hazards in terms of dust, toxins or accidents, are at greater risk in terms of coronary artery disease in middle life. This disease of the arteries supplying the heart produces anginal chest pain on effort, heart attacks and even sudden death in the middle age group. Here then, in terms of the United Kingdom Registrar General's social class groupings, we find that the first, second and third social classes are at greater risk to the health hazards of a sedentary life than the fourth and fifth classes. In other words, the executives, directors, managers, large and small organisation employers, scientists, professionals, clerks and supervisors are considerably worse off in respect of cardiac disease than semi-skilled workers and labourers. This brings us neatly back to our nineteenth century observer, Easton, and his people who reach old age only if they 'use much exercise'. This life-shortening effect of sedentary work is seen not only in the United Kingdom and in the United States but also in Europe and in Australia, New Zealand and Japan. The realisation that exercise might help to lower the incidence of heart disease in sedentary groups accounts for a resurgence of interest in sport, athletics, ball games, and even 'jogging' immediately after or before working hours. The present author has suggested in a previous book, *Snakes and Ladders*, that just as union rules or agreements have compelled employers to give coffee or tea 'breaks', so a statutory scheme for 'exercise breaks' during working hours could be devised and instituted for sedentary workers. A suitable slogan might be 'Exercise into your Eighties'.

The two manifestations of life-shortening effects of occupation on longevity appear to predominate in the male sex. Women seem to withstand these antagonistic effects better than their male contemporaries. This resistance may be genetic in origin or possibly hormonal—in terms of the female sex hormones, oestrogen and progestogen. We know from morbidity and mortality statistics that after the menopause, when the sex hormone levels drop steadily in women, the incidence of heart disease (and to a lesser extent, chest disease) rises to meet that of male contemporaries. Unfortunately, as we mentioned briefly in Chapter 6, physicians who have used this information in an applied way—giving female hormones to men with coronary artery and cardiac disease—have not demonstrated any real benefit in lengthening the male sufferers' lives.

Of the eleven occupational groups listed in the international classification, one potentially hazardous job must certainly be that of 'member of the armed forces' or, more simply, soldier, sailor or airman. The unbelievable carnage of nearly a million Frenchmen in the early part of World War I, and a comparable loss of life among Russian men in World War II, has been repeated on a relative scale in the so-called minor wars round the globe which have been 'contained'. With such figures for shortening of life, the persistence of the myth of longevity among the soldiery of many countries is hard to understand. This myth may derive from an acknowledged longevity among generals and senior commissioned officers who are kept 'protected' from front-line fighting for reasons of command continuity. A popular British ballad, however, tells us that 'old soldiers never die, they only fade away'. Certainly, the nineteenth century study showed many soldier centenarians, whose surnames covered many British areas. Anderson, Cumming, Simmons, Billings, Ramsay, Jackson and Craig are examples and there was even an Atkins (but not Tommy Atkins, the eponym for all British soldiery). Craig—Jack Craig —was a Scotsman who served in the Dragoons and fought in many fierce engagements throughout the eighteenth century. After retiring from active duty, he worked on farms as a labourer and reached 102 years before his death. The United States claims the longest living old soldier, J. B. Salling, a Tennessee 'reb', who reached his one hundred and thirteenth year; but a French soldier, Frederic Gardinville, who served in the army of Louis XV, also died at the reputed age of 113 years. Unhappily Gardinville died in 1851, whereas Salling died in 1959, so authentication of the latter's longevity record is on firmer ground.

The writer Thomas Carlyle, in his famous speech at Edinburgh University in 1886, declared that 'work is the grand cure of all the maladies and miseries that ever beset mankind'. Harold Laski, the twentieth-century English political scientist, put it more succinctly: 'hard work is the cure for most ills'. Neither of these famous men was speaking in terms of occupation and longevity, of course, for we have noted how work may be associated with many 'maladies and miseries'. Laski may well have been thinking of the effects of not being able to obtain work, since the social and economic miseries—as well as the mental stresses—of unemployment were all too familiar to the workers of Europe and North America in the 1920s and 1930s. Even today, we do not really know the effects of unemployment on the longevity status, particularly of men, and especially in the emerging but still undeveloped countries of Asia and Africa. In the advanced countries of the West and in parts of Africa and Asia, the problem of under-employment—due to mass production and automation processes, for example—may also ultimately affect the longevity status in the specific societies. Further, mass production, streamlining and automation processes have increased both leisure time and the likelihood of earlier retirement. The relationship of ageing to retirement, and to leisure, is not as straightforward as is popularly believed, and must therefore be our consideration in the next chapter.

JOB SATISFACTION

One other aspect of occupation and its relation to longevity is the influence, not of the job itself, but of the satisfaction of the work role. In the United Kingdom, for example, studies in the field of industrial psychology—like that of D. Hewitt and J. A. Parfit in 1953—have shown that workers in a small

organisation have a greater morale. Not only that, but in the
small enterprise body health as a whole is noticeably better.
The chances of job satisfaction might be thought to be greater
in small organisations if morale and health are better, but, as
A. Maslow pointed out in his study of motivation and personality in 1964, salary, wages, working conditions, inter-personal
relationships and job security all contribute to job satisfaction.
All these may be derived from any size of enterprise, depending on management attitudes and union influence, among
other factors.

In the Centre for the Study of Ageing and Human Development, at Duke Medical Centre in Durham, North Carolina,
the American worker E. B. Palmore has studied the physical,
mental and social factors for predicting longevity. Palmore
made a thirteen-year longitudinal study and reported that the
amount of variance in longevity explained by life expectancy
scores is increased by thirty-three per cent, when three other
scores are included in the equation. One of these turns out to
be the score for job satisfaction, which appears to be a factor
of more importance in predicting longevity in the male sex.
The other factors are physical functioning and intellectual
abilities, the former a factor in women especially. Similar
conclusions can be drawn from P. Storian's study in Rumania
in 1968, though job satisfaction is harder to define in the
political climate of Rumania.

We have already mentioned the important study carried
out by E. Pfeiffer in North Carolina which was an extension
of a longitudinal assessment at Duke University Medical
Centre in Durham of 'age-related changes in persons 60 years
and older'. Pfeiffer selected a number of distinctive attributes
and personal factors which appeared to influence survival of
certain individuals, who thereby constituted an 'elite group'.
In this particular study, the anticipated survival time of
Pfeiffer's select band of 'long livers' was nearly twenty years
for the female members and just over seventeen years for their

H

male counterparts. By comparison, the control group—otherwise matched for sex and age—had a survival time of just over five years for the women, and the very low figure of two and a half years for the men. In terms of our earlier discussion in this chapter, the individual occupation was not directly one of the significant factors in shortening, or lengthening, the life of a man or woman in either group. The job status did, however, appear to be an influential factor. Specifically, those men with lower occupational status than their contemporaries had a poorer survival time and were generally prone to an early demise.

Even within a given job status, there may be a differential of longevity the cause of which is not always readily understood. For example, in the National Health Service in the United Kingdom, a medical specialist practising psychiatry in hospital under the government's aegis—and known as a 'consultant psychiatrist'—is obliged to retire at the age of sixty years. By contrast, his colleagues in all the other specialties —medicine, surgery, obstetrics, paediatrics, orthopaedics, geriatrics, and many others—are not obliged to retire from National Health Service practice until the age of sixty-five years. A five year difference in practice represents a significant slice of working life yet, so far as the present writer can ascertain, no specific reason is given by the authorities administering the National Health Service for this compulsory early retirement for specialists in mental illness. The reader can, of course, draw the obvious conclusion that the stresses and strains of practising psychiatry take a greater toll in health— and therefore in potential longevity—than the practice of other medical specialties. There is a piece of evidence to support this: the high suicide rate among physicians practising psychiatry.

CHAPTER 11

A Long and Happy Retirement

THE LATER THE BETTER

SOME ORGANISATIONS HONOUR THE RETIRING OF A LONG-SERV-
ing employee with a certificate and a suitable gift, such as a
watch. This is generally cherished by the recipient, and may
be shown to visitors and relatives at appropriate moments in
the years after retirement. Other firms show no apparent
recognition for loyalty and long service. For example, the
present writer was taking a case history from a cheerful eighty-
three year old ex-cotton worker who told that he had worked
for over forty years in the same enterprise. On enquiry as to
what recognition there was at the end of that long service, the
writer was drily informed: 'five days notice to leave, doctor!'
Despite its humour, the remark happens to underscore a fact
noted—among others—by Peter Townsend in his famous
British study of a working-class district, *The Family Life of
Old People* (in Bethnal Green, London). This is the recognition that working-class men (particularly in the fourth and
fifth classes of the Registrar General's groupings) have been
made to retire against their conscious wish. If not so compelled, most of them indicated, they would have preferred to
go on working as long as health, strength and availability of
work permitted. Townsend reported several reasons for these
men not wishing to retire—social reasons, such as the com-
radeship and satisfaction of doing a job, the status and authority of being the breadwinner, and economic reasons, such as

maintenance of income for the family, and opportunities to enjoy more costly leisure interests.

In Great Britain in 1954, the then Ministry of Pensions and National Insurance investigated personal reasons for retiring or remaining at work. Nearly thirty thousand men and women participated voluntarily in this research study, and a wide variety of occupational groups were represented. The results showed that, even in the first social class, few really wanted to retire at the minimum age or at the compulsory age. Further, after the age of seventy, thirty per cent of men still preferred to carry on working. Even if we take into account the effects of economic change and monetary inflation, the professional class is less likely to wish to continue work for mainly economic or status reasons. It seems as if all social classes and both sexes prefer to go on working as long as possible, and retirement, far from meaning the withdrawal from customary occupation, implies a sense of guilt and inferiority. The Harley Street physician William Evans called it the shame of 'retreating from the contest' (of life) and the 'walking off the stage with humility'. In an earlier book, *Later Life: Geriatrics Today and Tomorrow*, the present writer described the contrast of 'coming home one day as the family breadwinner, a skilled employee, a favourite workmate, and waking up the next day as a fixed-income spouse, a retired employee, a forgotten workmate and a husband who is already in his wife's way as she does the home chores'. This can bring resentment, depression, loss of purpose and sometimes mental disaster to the man unprepared for the retirement phase.

Two factors have accentuated the problems of retirement at the present time. The physical and mental health of men and women in their sixties, compared with that of the same age group fifty years ago in the developed countries, is generally much improved. At the same time, mechanisation and automation, and the faster pace of trade, industry and commerce, have steadily lowered compulsory retirement ages to

65, 60 or even 55 years. This means that able, skilled and trained workers, with good physical and mental capabilities, are being released into a leisure existence for which they may be personally unprepared. Moreover, there may be inadequate community support or provision for such leisure time, and further the retirement period may nowadays last twenty, twenty-five or thirty years or even more.

PREPARING FOR RETIREMENT

Relatively few of today's very senior citizens have benefited from the newer approaches to retirement found in the urban industrialised societies of Europe, the North American continent and Australia, New Zealand and South Africa. Employers, doctors, public health workers, trade union men and educationalists have become increasingly aware of the need to develop a practical approach to the 'pre-retirement phase'. In individual industrial and commercial organisations, this may involve an 'easing-off' or 'phasing-out' process in different tasks in the three or four years up to official retirement age. This may take account of a need for slower paced work or lighter work, in factory settings, or reduced responsibilities or less onerous tasks, in clerical or professional enterprises. Shifts may be altered, and actual hours of working adjusted to a reduced or changing capacity.

Private companies and public enterprises in most of the advanced countries encourage employees in the pre-retirement phase to attend lecture courses on the problems of retirement and the means and services available to solve such problems. These courses may be organised internally in the enterprise, or arranged through local colleges or universities. Courses may be organised on a day-release basis, or on a night-class basis, and lecturers are drawn from the relevant spheres: mental health, physical health, social services, economic advisers, leisure 'experts', and people already retired who have 'good ideas' that can be adapted for new retirees.

National organisations in several countries, such as the American Association of Retired Persons, the Pre-Retirement Association in Great Britain, the European Federation for the Welfare of the Elderly in Switzerland, the Association Nationale des Anciens in France, and the West German equivalent, Lebensabend Bewegun, have all shown practical interest in the problems of retirement and retiring for the senior citizens of their populations. The United States' Council on Ageing emphasised in its first memorandum in the 1960s that there was an urgent need to find new ways of harnessing the skill of the ten per cent of the population that constitutes America's senior citizenry. In 1970, in Great Britain, the Institute of Personnel Management held a joint two-day symposium with the London Chamber of Commerce on the theme of managing retirement. In the talks and ensuing discussion, phrases like 'proper adjustment' and 'phased retirement' and 'policy of convenience' underlined aspects of the theme. At the 9th International Congress of Gerontology, held at Kiev in Soviet Russia in mid-1972, themes included 'the retirement process', 'income maintenance in retirement' and 'social welfare of the retired' among many others on the social science of ageing. Thus retirement and ageing are seen jointly as ongoing problems—and problems which will touch increasingly on all populations with a rising economic progress and consequent social changes, as well as on those with advanced economies.

RETIREMENT AND HEALTH

There is a popular notion that retirement, and particularly non-voluntary or premature retirement, is directly injurious to health and is life-shortening. Lay and professional persons typically remark that 'old John Brown was fit as a fiddle in his job until he had to retire at 70; then he died only a few

months later'. The clear implication is that the physical act
of retiring against his will so damaged John Brown's body
systems as to kill him prematurely. An American study by
Dr E. Shanas of Chicago University, over four years ago,
challenged this popular notion that retirement actually causes
poor health. Instead, Dr Shanas found that the correlation lay
in the fact that people in poor health or with definite physical
limitations had to retire, or were made to retire. The 1954
Ministry of Pensions study in Great Britain, mentioned above,
showed that chronic illness and general ill-health accounted
for fifty per cent of the reasons given by men in Class 1 who
had stopped doing their jobs at the minimum retirement age.
In Townsend's Bethnal Green study already mentioned, the
reverse situation was discovered: working-class men were able
to remain at work provided they remained in good health.
Professor Ferguson Anderson and Dr Nairn Cowan, in their
Scottish studies at the Rutherglen Preventive Clinic for the
over-fifty-fives, showed that ill-health in older men is an important factor in causing retirement. However, they concluded
that this reason for retirement is less common after the age of
64 years, and accounts for only a fifth of retirements between
65 and 85 years. They also confirmed the late Lord Beveridge's
view that the adverse influence of advancing years is seen less
when it is a question of retaining old employment than when
it is a question of finding new employers.

Anderson and Cowan also drew attention to the fact that
because an older worker is actually in employment, it does
not necessarily indicate that he is also in good health. Like
Townsend, they found that happiness among older men was
greater (what the social scientists call 'increased hedonic tone')
among those who remained at work than those who had
retired. Like other British researchers before and since, the
Scottish doctors concluded that 'the primary problem of retirement is the related mental stress rather than any physical
ill-health which may co-exist'. (The studies of W. Donahue

and others reported in 1960 in the United States suggested
that a fair proportion of old people feel in better health after
retirement, despite the fact that adjustment to retirement is
a major problem.) On the other hand, Dr I. W. Evans of
Aberdeen in Scotland has pointed out that none of the three
mental conditions—depression, anxiety and psychoneurosis—
for which men over 65 years most frequently consult doctors,
is related to occupation.

Another popular notion is that the effects of retirement on
women are not so dramatic or drastic as on men. Again,
Townsend's Bethnal Green study tended to confirm this. Both
his figures and those of the Ministry of Pensions study agree
that women more frequently retire voluntarily, and about fifty
per cent do so because of major or minor ill-health. Similar
conclusions in terms of social adjustment can be drawn from
the 1969 study of the 'ageing Australian' by S. J. Shepherd of
Victoria, Australia, and from J. Shanan's cross-cultural study
in Israel on both Afro-Asian groups and Europeans. Here is
another environmental pointer towards the longer survival of
women in the senior years.

The difficulties and problems of adjustment in retirement
are at their peak in the early years after discontinuing employment. The 80, 90 and 100 year olds are likely to have
come to terms with their non-work situation and status. Their
main activities and interests are either home-centred or
leisure-centred, that is, revolving around spouse, offspring,
chores, and home entertainments like radio and television—
or around club, pub, shops, garden and outside entertainments like bingo and cinema. There are also the parks, the
beaches and the organised entertainments of groups going
on vacations, trips, theatre outings and to musical events.
There are many factors which determine the degree of
participation by the senior and very senior citizen in both
home-centred and leisure-centred activities—social class, economic state, personality, urban or rural situation, being single

or married, for example. The most important factor of all, however, is physical mobility. Without continued physical mobility, it is very much harder (and less likely) for the very senior citizen to enjoy 'a long and happy retirement' which is the genuine wish bestowed upon him or her at a retirement presentation.

Before we go on to look at leisure in senior years, in retirement terms, we should remember that some groups of people continue 'their usual work' into very advanced age. The two outstanding groups are the creative persons—painters, writers, poets, sculptors, musicians—and the scientists—inventors, chemists and even a few physicians. For them, instead of the disengagement of retirement, there is often a change of intent and change of content, but a remarkable maintenance of drive. Referring once more to the Duke study reported by E. Pfeiffer in the United States, retirement or the likelihood of retirement is not mentioned as a significant criterion for membership of the elite group of survivors. This may act in a cryptic or less observable fashion, however, as Pfeiffer does mention that those with better 'life satisfaction' ratings have a higher survival rate. For the individual, life satisfaction itself includes a number of criteria, and at least one of these must refer to 'at work' or 'in retirement' hedonic tone. (Others are family and group role, achievement status, fulfilment of ambition, and less measurable criteria such as depth of creativity.)

A Rumanian study, undertaken by workers at the Bucharest Institute of Geriatrics, investigated 1,000 employees two years before their pensionable age point. The study was oriented both towards mental attitude and social behaviour in the pre-retirement work setting, and mental outlook and domestic behaviour in the home setting. As would be expected, many variables influenced the particular findings, so that—for example—the presence of ill-health or general well-being, the personality and temperament, and the social class in terms

of occupational status, all affected the results. This fits in
with the findings of Shanas and Townsend, as well as Anderson and Cowan. In Rumania, too, the notion corroborated
by Townsend—that women withstand retirement (or the
prospect of retirement) better than men—was reaffirmed.
This sociological survey was used as the basis of an organised
policy towards pre-retirees, undertaken in co-operation with
the management of the various works and businesses. Such
a policy included 'preparation for retirement' advice on
health, economics and social adjustment, and practical help
wherever problems arose or could be anticipated.

CHAPTER 12

Leisure, Time and Meaningful Activity

INCREDIBLE SHRINKING MAN

AMONG THE EARLIEST SCIENCE FICTION FILMS THAT APPEARED in the 1950s, one which fascinated many people was a story apparently based on the true report of a man exposed to radiation. The effect of this radiation was to reduce his physical frame. From that news item, the screenplay writer produced *The Incredible Shrinking Man*, a film which followed the gradual diminution in size of a happily married adult as a result of accidental exposure to a toxic spray. Using photographic special effects, the tale unfolded in a series of phases —disbelief, partial adjustment, search for an antidote, trial of antidote, failure to stop the effect, further adjustment, problems of a change of physical frame, frustrations and satisfactions, and the final path down to dissolution. The cinema goer was impressed by both the camera tricks and the acting, but inevitably, if he or she was at all moved by the film narrative, there came the realisation that here was a moral tale about the nature of man. There is a remarkable similarity between ageing man (or woman) and 'the incredible shrinking man'. There is the gradual or sudden realisation of growing and being old and a reaction of disbelief. A partial adjustment to the situation takes place, but retirement may undo or disturb the adjustment. Some antidote or preventative to retirement and growing old may be sought and tried, possibly with limited initial success. The effects of ageing continue, however, and further adjustment in the home and outside setting takes place. Changes in physical and mental mobility occur and have to be supported, or treated, or corrected. The old and very old person finds expected sources. The final path leads eventually to dissolution.

The analogy of the ageing person with the incredible shrinking man involves two factors of significance in all human lives: time and change. In the last chapter, we saw how several studies have underlined the occupation or job of work as the nucleus of a man's life, so that social and physical states are determined by being at work regularly. The worker's time at home and outside it is largely dictated by his job. When retirement arrives, the nuclear point on which the worker focuses his time usage is abruptly removed. This calls for either a new factor upon which to focus time usage or a reappraisal of time usage in general. Griffor, of Los Angeles in the United States, undertook a study of retired white-collar workers to try and determine how such retirees look at time in their 'new' state as compared with the period when they worked at a steady job. As might be expected, the reactions of the white-collar men varied in relationship to their own personality—outgoing, introverted, active, passive, for example—and according to the already firmly entrenched behaviour patterns of previous years. Sociological studies in skilled and semi-skilled workers in Europe, Japan and Great Britain over the past five years appear to confirm the importance of pre-retirement personality and behaviour in time usage when the man or woman is no longer tied to an occupation as the central point in his life.

TIME USAGE

Time for many people is divided into the 'now' period of immediate activity, the 'soon' period of tomorrow's activities and the 'later' period of activities months and weeks later. The past, for the active working person, only impinges on the 'now' and 'soon' in a minor or moderate way. For the older person, and particularly the retired older person, the 'past' is often a vivid part of the 'now'. Stories and events and people from the past intrude and colour the older person's present life time. D. N. Pakusch of Germany has pointed out the paradox that post-retirees have more time available to them (because they no longer work) but less time available to them (in terms of possible years ahead). She considers that this explains why some old people experience time shooting by at a helter-skelter pace while others feel the tortoise speed of each passing hour.

Peter Townsend described retirement as a 'social disaster' for many of the elderly working-class men looked at in his Bethnal Green study. This was not only because of loss of income and loss of status but also because they 'could not occupy their time satisfactorily'. C. Omachi of Japan studied the Japanese senior citizenry in both the metropolitan urban community of Tokyo and the less sophisticated city of Nagoya. He found that the more industrialised the area, the greater the appreciation of time usage. Omachi pointed out, however, that each culture has its own criteria for assessing the value and substance of time in old age. Even within national cultural boundaries, the use of time in a positive and meaningful way varies with religious, ethnic and social class factors. In the Stockport study mentioned earlier, the level of activities inside and outside the home was carefully assessed. The researchers, Brockington and Lempert, discovered that the extent of activities in general 'varied significantly with social class'. In fact, among the fourth and fifth social classes (semi-skilled and unskilled groups) in retirement, just over fifty per cent had more than two activities of a domestic or external kind, compared with nearly three-quarters of those in the first social class.

In terms of actual activities, Omachi found that the top class people (to use his own phrase) enjoyed reading, and creative work like painting and writing, as well as keeping up with trends and news in their own professional fields. They also enjoyed giving tuition and guidance and assisting in voluntary services. All such activities were affected by the mobility and independence of the 'top people' as individuals. In the less educated social class (whom we might label 'not such top people', by contrast), activities tended to be home oriented—sewing and mending and knitting, and household chores—and passive—listening to the radio and watching television. This second pattern could be countered by recruitment to 'senior citizen clubs' which encourage outings, social events and more active hobbies. In fact the Japanese urban pattern was not dissimilar to the British pattern—with the addition of football pool coupon filling, card playing, and indoor board games like checkers and chess at home, and watching sports fixtures and going to public houses and gardens. Even in their eighties, the 'top people' may go out motoring, and visit the theatre and cinema.

Dr H. Behrends of Bonn in Germany, studying post-retirement and older senior citizens, pointed out that society at large can impose a pattern of life (and of time usage) on such old people in several ways. A general ill-feeling of young people towards the idea of old people partaking in regional (or local) cultural and social events may prevent such old people knowing of these 'coming events'. Information on available social help and economic support may not reach old people either, reducing independence and mobility, so that time usage is focused drearily in a four-walled room of the house and the 'present' rarely changes. The expected role of an individual old person depends on his or her social setting.

For example, the old person living in a residential home is expected to be a friendly, conforming member of the group of residents—taking part in organised activities, keeping to the rules and regulations governing food, visitors, going out times, personal belongings, and generally being a 'co-operative old soul'. Another example is the old mother, a surviving grandparent, taken to live with a daughter and her husband and family—expected to help with the family chores but not to organise the household, to give advice when asked for it but not to interfere in decisions, to join in the family activities but not to be a nuisance or too obtrusive, 'a dignified old figurehead'. Yet another example is the elderly married couple, living in a rented apartment or home, on a fixed income being eroded by inflation—expected to maintain their home and themselves in good appearance, to be a 'Darby and Joan' but not to show physical expressions of real love, to help out with babysitting and looking after the grandchildren but not to have any say in their upbringing, a 'dear old dad and mum'. It is little wonder that senior and very senior citizens can talk so bitterly about loneliness in the midst of many. So often, their expected role is that of 'shadow people' whose time and energy only has substance in terms of what others—the institution, the family, the social group —give them to do.

The correlation of meaningful activity and time usage in the possible roles of old people in advanced urbanised society is being studied more carefully in the light of what we have said in the last two paragraphs. We know that tribal societies in the underdeveloped parts of Africa, for example, still look to the senior members as the 'wise elders' who can advise and teach and encourage the continuity of tribal traditions. In such primitive cultures, the 'generation gap' is easier to bridge and old people maintain status and power and receive respect and esteem. In advanced societies, the generation gap between parent and child is large enough, but between grandparent and grandchild there is a yawning chasm. Power and prestige is measured in terms of success in the mass media or professional life, wealth in terms of acquired or inherited cash in the bank, and influence in terms of politics and the establishment. Age, that is chronological seniority, does not appear to come into it. Even students, the rebels and revolutionaries of stable societies, often see old age as 'conservatism' and 'sterility' only.

GETTING ORGANISED

The reaction of old people (and their younger 'supporters') to being either rejected or treated as a 'minority group' has developed in several directions. In local areas, there has been the development of community centres for senior citizens, of over-sixties' clubs, retired employees' organisations, charity senior citizen groups and church and ethnic societies for older people. For those mobile enough to reach them—by walking, public transport or private car—such clubs and societies provide meeting places for local citizens with common backgrounds and common interests. The clubs counter the feeling of loneliness, uselessness, and not being wanted, and give a positive point in time at which to expect enjoyment. In many places, such groups foster or rekindle pride in the local community and a sense of belonging. They give opportunities for continuing forms of self-expression through self-help and helping other members, so that time usage becomes important again and activity more meaningful.

In regional areas, reaction to the intended or unmeaning rejection of themselves as old people in society has led to the socio-economic policy of 'middle-aged' and 'senior citizen' residential communities. These may be planned developments by local government authorities, with purpose-built apartments and bungalows, community and shopping centres, a warden, supervisory helpers, medical and nursing attendants available, and sheltered or hospital accommodation if and when required. The Scandinavians were pioneers in this direction, as were the Scots. Of the earliest examples of this form of 'retirement village' two were built as long ago as 1934 and 1938, Old People's Town in Copenhagen and Elderslie at Glasgow in Scotland. Both are still functioning in an updated form today. Among the best of modern examples of this form of living are the Dutch local authority projects in Amsterdam and Rotterdam.

On an even larger scale, in the private enterprise field, are the now famous Golden Age, Leisure World and Sun City developments which provide accommodation, amenities, and leisure facilities aimed specifically at the middle-aged and senior citizens of the United States. Initially built in areas of Southern California, Florida and Arizona, such complexes have spread north and east, or have been copied by enterprising developers in suburban areas of larger cities.

The national reaction to apparent rejection of old people as proper citizens of the state has been the development of organisations with a fixed interest in one or more aspects of ageing. These organisations can act as watchdogs, gingergroups and promoters of schemes and developments in the social, economic and cultural fields affecting the retiring, the retired, and all elderly citizens. These may have a medical bias—such as the British Geriatrics Society, the Japan Gerontological Society, the New Zealand Society for the Study of Ageing, the American Geriatrics Society, and the similar societies of Australia, South American and European countries and the Soviet Union. They may have a research bias— such as the British Society for Research on Ageing, and the Swedish, Swiss and Soviet Gerontological Research Societies, as well as the American Gerontological Society. They may have a socio-economic bias—such as the National Council on Ageing of the United States, Age Concern (formerly the National Old People's Welfare Council) of Great Britain, the National Old People's Welfare Councils of Australia, the Association Nationale des Anciens in France—and voluntary

J

organisations in many countries corresponding to the British
Women's Royal Voluntary Service, Red Cross and St John
Ambulance Societies, Round Table and Rotary groups, the
Central Council for the Disabled, and the National Council
of Social Services. (There are also various 'housing scheme'
organisations in the United Kingdom with equivalents in
Europe, like the religious Homes for the Aged, Mutual House-
holds Association, The Abbeyfield Society and the Hanover
Housing Association.)

Such organisations keep an eye on social benefits and pensions provided by governments; on special economic forms
of transport, homes and amenities; on nutrition through
luncheon clubs, meals-on-wheels and charitable food kitchens;
and on physical support through 'good neighbour' schemes,
'boarding out' schemes, sick visiting, and liaison with local
government authorities providing domestic help, nursing
aids, and temporary hostel care. They also support the local
clubs and societies which provide social activities, outings
and cultural amenities. International co-ordinating bodies
also exist to promote the interest and welfare of senior citizens,
such as the International Association of Gerontology, and
the European Federation for the Welfare of the Elderly.

In Australia, for example, which has a ten per cent
population of pensionable age—like so many other developed nations we have noted—many senior citizens enjoy their
leisure at social clubs. These are open daily, and are generally
supported by local authorities, either indirectly by finance
or directly by supplying a paid organiser. A state like Victoria, for example, may have several hundred clubs scattered
throughout its area. The clubs are frequently housed in purpose-built premises, and are sited with an eye on central
location—for access to shopping facilities, and for amenities
like libraries. As in the United Kingdom or in Sweden, the
premises may be used to provide subsidised wholesome meals
for the senior citizens attending. As kitchen facilities may not

always be present (or, indeed, staff to man them), the familiar 'meals-on-wheels' mobile type of service may be employed to create a 'luncheon club' facility. Such meals services are not confined to the eastern states—Perth in Western Australia, for example, and Hobart in the isle of Tasmania also have useful meals-on-wheels services.

AT HOME

Domiciliary aid services such as we have been describing in this book—home aides, home nurses, home helps and meals supplies—are based in many countries on local and municipal authorities as the central organising bodies. They provide the finance and expertise, with or without the support and manpower of interested voluntary groups, to initiate and maintain such services. Several years ago, in an article in the *British Hospital Journal and Social Service Review*, the present writer suggested that all supportive services for the senior citizen in the community should be co-ordinated through, and emanate from, the hospital department or unit concerned with elderly citizens, usually the department of geriatrics. In Launceston, Tasmania, the Australians showed that such an organisation from within the hospital setting could function effectively. In the United Kingdom, however, as a result of the findings of the Seebohm Committee on Local Authority and Allied Personal Social Services, the supportive services for old people (and others in need) are co-ordinated by a Director of Social Services in each local authority area—and are generally divorced from the hospital setting. Liaison does take place among departments in hospital and in the local authority, of course, but this is not 'integration'.

BACK TO WORK

For some senior citizens, the only meaningful leisure activity

is a return to some form of work. Both the opportunities
and the physical and mental capacity for doing this tend to
diminish in the late seventies and eighties, and are certainly
very limited in both ways in the ninth decade. (A recent
news item in the English press, however, stated that one of
the spectators at a works retirement ceremony for a 65 year
old employee was his 91 year old father who was still actively
employed in his trade.) Nevertheless, part-time employment
can be and is undertaken by retired senior citizens. This
can be related to seasonal demands—such as in enterprises
at seaside resorts or in the Post Office just before Christmas.
For men it may mean such traditional 'old age' jobs as
works messengers, night watchmen, caretakers, light cleaning
workers, elevator attendants, doorkeepers, porters (of the
light work variety), car park attendants, and handbill or
sandwich board advertising men. Alternatively, as F. Le Gros
Clark pointed out in his various studies of older men at work,
employers in industry and commerce may give light employment to elderly unskilled men in the light assembly and
stores sections, and continue using skilled and semi-skilled
employees well past their sixty-fifth years until physical and
mental health changes necessitate a decision to retire. In the
very heavy industries such as iron and steel works, mining
and quarrying enterprises, and in highly automated plant,
the opportunities for continued employment of much older
men is minimal.

Elderly women, on the other hand, who are physically and
mentally well enough to undertake jobs outside the home,
often take on domestic-style work such as part-time cleaning,
in offices, shops and factories, and canteen or kitchen or
cooking assistant work. Part-time teaching—often at home—
of music, languages, elocution and other arts is also undertaken by those with appropriate skills and qualifications.
Sheltered workshops for retired senior citizens of both sexes
first began under the aegis of industrial employers, like the

famous Rolls Royce concern in Great Britain, which used to arrange a special area of the factory to utilise the skills of retired employees in a given number at one or more times each week. A parallel idea was the setting up of community centres whose facilities were used to 'take in' light work—toy making, craft work, labelling, for example—for women and men attenders who were paid on a money per item basis.

In London, both the Employment Fellowship and Rotary International run other versions of sheltered workshops, and the report in 1965 from Luton (on employing elderly persons in an industrial county borough of England) showed that the majority of retirees wanted work and many were enabled to obtain it by a variety of local organisations, such as 'Vespers'. E. King and H. Rusalem of New York, in the United States, carried out a project—reported in 1969—to determine the possibilities of making a new career in old age. The project was designed to create a group of persons trained to help the physically housebound as 'personal aides', and the age range of those enrolled was wide, sixties to nineties. King and Rusalem reported considerable success with their project, the main cause of defaulting—as we might reasonably expect—being ill-health in the older members. They concluded that 'vocational development into new areas need not terminate in old age'. In Australia, New Zealand and South Africa, the idea of workshops for the elderly—both physical work and social projects—has been taken up and adapted to local needs and conditions. Apart from the financial 'rewards' of such workshops, and their help in combating 'leisure loneliness', there is the factor of exercise contributing to health, and the benefit of the return to being a community member, observing and observed.

The American psychiatrist A. R. Martin, of New York, has defined leisure as 'an actively receptive condition of the whole personality', which is present at different times in daily life and for longer periods in a given year. The senior citizens of today in the advanced countries are the 'greatest leisure class' in society. Because so many retirees have a fixed income, they have also been called the 'first impoverished leisure class'. Perhaps, when Employment Exchanges, Labour Bureaux, and private enterprise job-finding organisations in the advanced countries start to include—as a matter of course—senior citizens in their personnel throughput, we shall see that 'society in general' has begun to come to terms with an aged group which still wants to be employed. Then the familiar process will have ensued—in which solutions to national problems are first tackled by voluntary groups locally and regionally; eventually governments take a direct interest, at which point statutory provisions are instituted to enforce the solutions, and the government congratulates itself on its 'original and enlightened programme' for old people.

CHAPTER 13

Environment for Age

AIR, WATER AND WEATHER

THERE IS A DELIGHTFUL MOMENT IN THE MUSICAL *Camelot*, when King Arthur of the Round Table tells us how Merlin once changed him into a bird, so that he could appreciate how it feels to soar freely into the sky. The wild bird enjoys its ability to match wing against wind, to fly in the sun and shelter in the rain, to sleep by night and travel on the wing by day—and to hunt its prey as and when it can, and must. This is a poetic view of environment in its natural state, to which a living creature can readily and reasonably adjust and hope to survive to its natural limits. Unfortunately, for man as an individual living creature, mankind's technical progress has vastly altered any natural environment. This is apparent not only in heavily industrialised and vastly urbanised regions in various countries but also in the rural and agricultural areas, whose soil and water supplies for example may be contaminated by modern additives, fertilisers and conservation processes. In other words, there are few places in any continent where the inhabitants have a natural, unspoiled, untainted environment, which allows them each the possibility of attaining maximum human longevity. It is paradoxical that the introduction of mass campaigns against infectious diseases in rural areas of underdeveloped countries brings with its success a necessary chemical pollution of the environment—as in the anti-cholera campaign in India, for instance, when lime and insecticides were spread in the open drains. Even the stress-free environment of our celebrated Georgian centenarians has been altered, by the collectivising of their farming methods, and the mechanisation of various kinds in the poultry and livestock areas.

In the nineteenth century, health 'experts' paid attention not only to diet and exercise but also to the air of the environment, and to the 'waters'. We have earlier mentioned, in passing, the idea that water from natural springs has special health-giving (and life-lengthening) properties. The ancient Romans practised balneology, and in more modern times the cult of 'taking the waters' was practised all over Europe, both in the original Spa in Belgium and in the many other spas— Bath in England, Wiesbaden in Germany and Auvergne in France for example. Whatever the benefits of drinking natural spring waters, if any, there is no doubt that the hot spring waters improved health in three ways. Firstly, there was the purely hygienic aspect of people actually removing clothing to bathe. Next, there was the effect of hot water warmth on stiff and ageing joints and muscles. Lastly, there was the (often unacknowledged) psychological effect of the social gathering, whose conviviality and mutual sympathy produced emotional uplift. Admittedly, the spas were mainly the province of the upper classes of middle and later life; but the principle of bathing in spring water and taking thermal therapy was available to the rural living populations of lower social classes, too, and in country areas was often claimed by very senior citizens as one of the factors contributing to their longevity. As far as 'fresh air' was concerned, John Sinclair, another nineteenth century English knight with strong views on pathways to health, tied up the air and water views very neatly. He advised that there is 'no air as pure and wholesome, as in the neighbourhood of a small stream, running over a rocky or pebbly bottom'. Watkinson, a physician contemporary of Sir John Sinclair, studied the atmosphere of Ireland and described it as a constant 'balneum vaporis'. Nevertheless he considered that the moisture and the temperate quality of the air was a 'great advantage' to them. This was really a tribute to an atmospheric temperature which avoids extremes, rather than a paean for Irish rain.

DOMICILE

The American retirees who make their way from the east coast and midwest to California, Arizona and Florida nowadays, must be unimpressed by the virtues of damp, temperate climates as an environment for age. Equally, the wealthier European retirees who make for the sun of Portugal, Italy and the south of France must be very sceptical about the longevity value of British or German rainfall. Certainly, as we have noted before, senior and very senior citizens dislike extremes of temperature and moisture. The effects of extremes in cold seem harder to withstand at any age, but more so in the seventies and eighties and nineties. This is one of the reasons why, in cooler climates, older people are particularly interested in the heating arrangements of their dwellings, whether home, hostel, nursing home, extended care facility, apartment, bungalow or hospital. In the variably polluted, variably warm, variably damp climate and atmosphere of so many countries, the form and content of domicile, and the form of heating in that domicile, are of singular importance in the environment for age.

In all the advanced countries with a high or rising percentage of senior citizens, national surveys have confirmed and underlined the special needs of old people in any public or private housing programme. In Great Britain immediately after World War II, the Rowntree Committee suggested that five per cent of any new housing development should have its design adapted for senior citizens. The fruits of this recommendation are only beginning to be felt in the major

European conurbations, as post-war housebuilding rates have increased to levels like 10.7 dwellings per 1,000 population in West Germany, 11.9 per 1,000 in France, and 11.4 per 1,000 in Sweden. Both the United Kingdom and the United States, with levels of 7.1 and 8.3 dwellings per 1,000 population respectively, have been less able to cope with the housing needs of the elderly section of their population. This was so until at least the late 1960s, despite the needs revealed by extensive social surveys, like those of H. Chalke and B. Benjamin, or the Townsend and Lempert studies, or the J. Frush study, on either side of the Atlantic.

Ideally, the form and content of housing matches the social needs, physical and mental health, economic status and income, social class, and required amenities for the individual older person. Matching social needs means considering such factors as single or married accommodation, desired levels of privacy within households and among neighbours, proximity of shops and services, accessibility of private and public transport and ready availability of medical doctors, dentists or other professionals. Location of leisure facilities and provision of entertainments are equally important. Matching physical and mental health to housing implies taking into account degree of mobility—full, housebound, wheelchairbound, chairbound, bedbound; ability to cook, clean, wash, dress, negotiate ramps, and carry out the general activities of daily living; capacity to make decisions, recall recent matters and manipulate devices; need and ability to live alone, or with a companion, or in a gregarious setting; and presence or absence of incontinence, and other 'anti-social' habits. Matching housing to economic status and income involves such factors as occupational pension, retirement pension, income from savings and available capital, owner of own home or apartment, renting private or local authority or government accommodation, living in fixed accommodation or in mobile homes, and supplementary income available from

part-time work, from relatives or from social services or charitable sources. Matching social class includes: availability of
types of accommodation in given regional sectors; voluntary
housing associations and ethnic or society-organised associations organising 'social class' home building; and awareness
of problems in social class 'mixing' by those who plan government or local authority developments—hostels, apartments
or warden or manager supervised homes. Finally, matching
the required amenities for the older person depends on all
the other factors—social, health, economic, class—but also on
the previously available amenities in terms of hygiene, diet,
leisure and outside or home interests.

The studies already mentioned, and personal assessments
made by the present writer in Scandinavia, Europe and the
United States, confirm how far ideal housing, for senior and
very senior citizens, lies from the form and content which
actually exists. The terraced brick homes, dank, decaying and
substandard, in the mill towns of Lancashire, England, in
the late 1960s, were not dissimilar to the row homes of the
older parts of Baltimore, Maryland in the United States. The
grubby, unhygienic, ill-equipped and dilapidated flats in the
east end of Glasgow, Scotland in the early 1960s were not
dissimilar to the odoriferous, run-down, sleazy apartments in
New York city in the United States. The over-large Victorian
mansions, run-down and impossible to manage for very senior
citizens, with no servants, fixed incomes and indifferent health,
in London and surrounding counties of England, are not
dissimilar to the over-large colonial homes, decaying and un-
manageable, for the senior citizens of Long Island in New
York state. In all the advanced countries, there is still a surprising contrast between the wealthier senior citizen or the
retiree from the upper social classes, and the poorer old
person or retiree from the lower social classes. Government
agencies and local authorities cannot hope to match the de
luxe apartments of a Sun City, or the luxuries of a gadget-

filled, richly-furnished, multiple amenity private nursing
home, or the well-staffed, opulently equipped purpose-built
institutions of particular religious and ethnic groups. Instead
they have to consider the matching of available funds, allo-
cated from taxes and rates, to the population of old people
they service—and see how efficiently yet humanely the social,
environmental and economic needs of the many can be fulfilled. Such official bodies are less able to take account of
cultural needs, individual personalities, group desires or relatives' wants, but try not to ignore such factors where possible.
Where official planners have accepted the need for clusters of
'senior citizen housing' (sometimes called age-homogeneous
accommodation), there has been a tendency to build these as
complexes, moderately or markedly isolated from the mixed-
age community. As Hamovitch and co-workers at the University of Southern California have pointed out, such physical
isolation leads to loneliness and to mental and social deprivation. There is loss of confidence and of status, and a general
decline in the quality of life. More recently, both private
and public housing for older people, while still in age-group
clusters, has been set down as part of general housing rede-
velopments, or new housing facilities in central or suburban
areas.

THE THREE STATIONS OF HEALTH

No organiser of urban renewal projects which include an 'old
age housing development' has suggested that such a development might be tailored in terms of, say, decades: a group in
their seventies here, a smaller group in their eighties there,
a still smaller group in their nineties here and a tiny group
in their hundreds there. This would be patently absurd
because, as we have noted earlier, chronological age is a poor
guide to physical and mental state in senior years—and, of
course, is no guide to social and cultural needs and socio-

economic status. Yet planners and developers in some areas in various countries have literally planned for an 'old age group' as if senior citizens were, sex excepted, a homogeneous group with near-identical needs in form and content of housing. This has led to the extraordinary situation in Great Britain, for example, of old people who are well enough to live in their own homes—if supported by suitable community services—being admitted to local authority welfare homes; and old people who require the sheltered semi-dependent environment of local authority welfare homes, remaining in hospital 'long-stay' or extended care accommodation through lack of 'places' in the welfare homes. It is only since housing and social planners have been made aware of what has been called elsewhere 'the geriatric continuum', that a variety of housing has been made available in senior citizen complexes. By the geriatric continuum, we mean a two-way life flow, touching on the three stations of 'effective health' defined by I. Williams, in his 1971 study on the care of the elderly in general medical practice. Station 1 is when the senior citizen has no incapacitating illness, is independently mobile, can attend to personal service and shopping needs, and has a cheerfully orientated mental state. Station 2 is when the senior citizen has illness present but is coping with life, can cook and do housework, has mental decline but is able to manage his own hygiene, has restricted physical movements, and is housebound. Station 3 is when the senior citizen has incapacitating physical illness, severe mental disturbance, general restriction of body movements and is unable to cook, do housework and attend to personal needs and hygiene. Just because the citizen is in the old age category, it does not mean that he or she is fixed at the one station. Modern health and welfare approaches should permit the line through the stations to run backwards and forwards, with suitable therapy.

The housing complex for the elderly in the environs of Amsterdam in the Netherlands is a good example of 'matching the stations of effective health' by an appropriate environment. In one area, fronting a grassy garden, are houses and maisonettes occupied by elderly senior citizens, married and in their seventies and eighties—all belonging to the Station 1 category of effective health. On the opposite side of the grassed garden is a low-rise building (four floors only) served by elevators. Each floor has a series of small apartments, suitable for one-person or two-person accommodation, and small lounges and dining rooms, for community usage, at intervals between the apartments. These are tenanted by the Station 2 category of senior citizens who can make simple meals but are supplied with one cooked meal per day, and given other household help and medical attention if required. There is a community hall for leisure and cultural activities situated on the first floor, and services like hair-setting and facial 'treatments' are provided on the spot in a beauty parlour. All the apartments are radio-linked to the staff attendants who keep a watchful eye on the resident tenants. Those in Station 3 category are admitted to—and discharged from—a suitable hospital in close proximity to the main senior citizen housing area. This allows older citizens to observe that hospitals really can benefit them in diagnosis and treatment, and that they are no longer the unwholesome 'antechambers to the hereafter' which once used to be the case.

Other model forms are used in different countries, for example the Swedish complexes which are sometimes based round 'regional centres', the English complexes which are based on an 'old people's home' (hostel), or the American complexes based on 'service areas'. Such arrangements invariably have warden or manager supervision, with nursing and medical help available if required, and a concentration of social and medical services, amenities and leisure facilities. These complexes all take account, in their own way, of the category of effective health stations within which would-be tenants fall.

SAFETY IN THE HOME

As regards the form of housing, the aim of designers looking
at a suitable environment for age must be 'safety and sim-
plicity'. For example, good illumination by lighting and
windows, especially at changes of floor level, and ease of
obtaining light by simple cords and switches, are very important. Storage of utensils, materials and clothes should
permit easy access, avoidance of climbing or undue bending,
and ease of visibility. Cookers should have built-in safety
devices, and controls that can be managed by stiff-jointed or
disabled persons. The research group at Cornell University
in New York in the United States has looked carefully at
internal design of houses, producing criteria for design of
special rooms, as in the Kira report on the bathroom. Certainly shower and bathing facilities should include simply-
operated temperature control of water supply, easy access and
easy egress from the bath or shower, safety supporting rails
and handles, non-slip bases, bath seating and bidet, and
water closets with support handles. Floors generally should
be non-slip, easily cleaned, and warm and colourful in all
rooms. Internal ramps call for supporting handrails, and steps
should be at a minimum, well-lit, shallow and broad with
support rails. Such ideal internal facilities can be incorporated in purpose-built accommodation for senior and very
senior citizens. Houses and apartments in which older people
live, not specially built for their use, can be suitably adapted
and altered. This is provided the owner—if it is not the
senior citizen—agrees to such alterations, and provided the
older person agrees to take adaptation advice, can learn to
manage the mechanics of safety devices and is willing to
spend the money, if he or she is the owner-occupier. Just as
we have noted earlier that the time to plan for retirement
is well before the actual moment, in middle years, so the
time to plan for a safe and suitable home for senior years

is also in middle age. Local authorities in several advanced countries give financial support for such alterations for safety in the home.

WARMTH

The heating of the home is the other major protective item in the environment for age. In semi-mediterranean climates, or in climates with extreme external temperatures, the ideal system is an air-conditioning unit that controls an even flow of suitably warm or cool air throughout the various rooms. In temperate climates—and in the cooler evenings of warm climates—there is a twin concentration on heat conservation and heat production. Conservation methods include draught sealing, cavity wall filling, and double or triple glazing of individual windows. Heating methods—gas, electric or oil-fired central heating, with or without ducted air—should aim to keep the room temperature near 21 degrees centigrade for senior citizens, and concentrate on avoiding a cold air flow on the lower part of the body. Electric underfloor heating has been installed in many European old age housing developments, and has been much appreciated, so long as costs have been subsidised or kept low. In European countries, many old people still want 'visible' heat appliances, such as radiant heaters of the gas or electric type, and even open coal, coke or log fires—though these are anti-safety forms of heating for older people (and for children, too).

Senior citizens, and especially the over-eighties, cannot stand extremes of temperature because of the poorer functioning of the human body's thermostat (in the central nervous system), because of a lessened ability to sweat or constrict blood vessels and retain heat, and often because of diminished body mass and protective fat. Despite this, older people may economise on heating their homes by switching off all heating at night, allowing the room temperature to drop sharply. Unfortunately neither nightwear nor bedclothes may compensate for this temperature drop, and the environment is then potentially dangerous at night.

THE COST OF COMFORT

One problem that has arisen in the past, and still does, is the cost of capital outlay on, or the cost of rental of, new purpose-built housing for senior citizens. This is particularly under-lined where the older person has been living in poor property where rentals were very modest, or in unsuitable older housing which belongs to him but is not *per se* high in market value. Then, however attractive the special housing units may be in terms of comfort, amenities and safety, the older person or older couple may turn down the offer of new rented housing at much higher rents or not apply to purchase a more expensive unit in the new setting. Various schemes have been evolved to overcome such economic objections or financial strains in the re-housing of older people in appropriate new property. In the United Kingdom, for example, aid towards both rent and rates is forthcoming from the Supplementary Benefits Commission of the Social Security government de-partment, where this is deemed appropriate. This naturally implies an assessment of the personal means and equity of the older person and, the easy availability of credit ratings on individuals today notwithstanding, a senior citizen may reject such a 'means test'. Thus pride and a wish for privacy may prevent the success of such an approach.

Another source of aid for older persons who wish to enter, say, a hostel or old people's home accommodation, has been from voluntary bodies. These have often been based on a religious or ethnic grouping, such as the Quaker Homes, or the Catholic Homes, or the Jewish Homes for the aged, or homes run by particular religious orders. They may also be based on professional groupings, or on artistic groupings, such as the Motion Picture Country Home in Woodland Hills,

K

California, or the Musician Benevolent Fund Homes in the
United Kingdom. Capital subsidies for housing schemes for
the elderly may be offered by the state authorities, as for
example in Western Australia, both to voluntary organisations
and bodies who inaugurate their own housing care projects,
and to the local authorities. The latter may be involved in
general rehousing from poorer property and can benefit where
special old people's housing units are incorporated in the
main scheme. Low-cost housing 'for all' is a familiar political
promise in many advanced and emergent countries, but is not
always fulfilled. Perhaps if it were called 'housing for increased
longevity', the money might be forthcoming.

HUMAN CONTACT

In the national and local newspapers and some national and
local journals of such countries as Sweden, Denmark, Germany, the United States and the United Kingdom, we find
advertisements in the 'personal' columns for a 'suitable friend
or companion' for the lady or gentleman advertising. This is
a direct attempt on the part of lonely people, often middle-
aged or senior citizens, to overcome their isolation and mean-
ingless passing of each day. Again, such seekers after companionship may utilise the services of friendship bureaux or
marriage bureaux or contact agencies. The latter may be
better equipped through 'experience and assessment' to match
up the enquirers and make the element of 'blind dating' less
hazardous. The leisure and social clubs for senior citizens
afford a less 'obvious' method of making opposite-sex acquaint-
anceships but may just as frequently be the instrument of
second marriages or new couple arrangements. Of course, the
older person, if female, may be advertising for a female companion, either in lieu of a friend cum nurse or in lieu of a
housekeeper. Well-to-do older persons, otherwise alone, may
be able to afford to pay such a companion for her duties as

well as offering her board and lodgings.

Another idea to combat isolation and loneliness in the single or widowed elderly person is what has come to be known as 'the boarding out scheme for the elderly'. Either through the agency of a voluntary organisation—like an Old People's Welfare Council—or through the resources of a local authority, an elderly man or woman may be accommodated in a private home as a 'special boarder'. (This private home is not, of course, that of the older person's relative or friend.) A great deal of care is taken by the organisers of such 'boarding out' schemes to see that the home, the 'hostess', and the senior citizen boarder are compatible. (The process recalls the care taken by Adoption Societies in selection of child and selection of would-be parents in most advanced countries.) Where boarding-out schemes are organised by voluntary bodies, a financial contribution to their support may be made by the local authority. From a purely economic point of view, it is less costly to have an older citizen 'boarded out' in a private home than in an old people's hostel. From the senior citizen's viewpoint, provided the 'match' is successful, he or she may be much happier as an adopted member of a private household than in the less private community of a hostel setting.

'A COTTAGE BY THE SEA'?

In 1968, in England, the National Corporation for the Care of Old People brought together a representative 'study group' to consider the matter of retirement of English people to coastal resorts. The group included public health doctors, physicians in geriatric medicine, social service officers, representatives from the department of social security, staff of voluntary societies, interested local tradespeople, and local authority members. The governmental side was represented by officials from the government departments for housing and health. They were especially concerned with the pattern of

frequent retirement to the south-east coastal towns in England, which may produce an 'imbalance' in the proportion of
retired elderly people to the numbers of working people and
schoolchildren. This puts an extra strain on the social services,
such as home helps or local authority welfare homes, and on
the domiciliary health support services, such as home nurses,
health visitors and family doctors. These 'additional strains'
are less than one might expect, since a fair preponderance of
retirees are in the Registrar General's classes 1 and 2, and so
are able to support themselves financially and seek private
help. Such upper-class retirees live in their own properties, or
in residential hotels or guest houses. However, though there
were fewer homes and apartments to let for rent in the 1950s,
the late 1960s saw official projects by the Greater London
Council to re-house many London people at the coast. Such
dwellings were available on an appropriate rental basis.

The reasons for wishing to retire to the coast found by the
study group did not particularly include the weather—a
normal English preoccupation, because of its variability, un-
reliability and unpredictability. Certainly, the south-east coast
is warmer than the north-west coast but usually by a few
degrees at best. Some admitted that retiring to the coast was
the result of previous pleasurable memories of seaside trips or
coastal vacations. For others, it was the availability of leisurely
sea-side amenities compared with the continual hustle and
bustle of main towns in the interior. Some also had moved to
be near relatives who lived on the south-east coast. Unfortunately, some old people had come to regret retiring away from
familiar places and people of a lifetime, and were suffering
loneliness and isolation. The popularity of 'The Haven' as a
name for a retirement dwelling on the south-east coast of
England is apparently not always justified. Some old people
were also experiencing economic difficulties in paying the
higher rents demanded for (non-local authority) apartments
or places in guest houses during the 'summer season', when

the coastal resorts catered for holidaymakers and vacationers of a younger age group. Then, financially embarrassed, the older people had to migrate temporarily from the coastal area to cheaper inland accommodation.

THE TRANSPORT PROBLEM

This study group helped to expand the information on retirement mobility trends in the United Kingdom. It also underlined the increased scale on which social, housing and medical problems were occurring in 'unplanned' retirement areas, where initially little attention had been given to the 'risks and needs' mentioned earlier in this chapter. One aspect that was not mentioned by this particular study group was taken up by another group—the Civic Welfare Services Committee—in 1969 in the north-west coastal resort of Southport in England. This was the problem of transport. Few over-seventies and virtually no over-eighties had their own car transport, so most relied on municipal bus services to travel to shops and general amenities and to see relatives. In that community, as is so often the case, the bus routes and stopping places were often too distant, relatively speaking, to be used satisfactorily. The wealthier old people could still utilise taxis and private hire cars but the less well-to-do were unable to afford regular expenditure of this form. They either relied upon relatives or kind volunteers, or suffered more isolation and loneliness.

Diminished public transport in all the advanced countries of Europe and the Americas particularly affects the senior citizen population. It is of little use to provide 'senior citizen permits' for reduced fares between certain hours if the bus stops are too far away to be readily reached. There is also the physical problem of stepping on and off buses, if the joints are stiff, the muscles are less firm and the general pace of movement is slower. High steps, automatic doors and sharp starting and braking can all dissuade older people from bus travel.

CHAPTER 14

Companionship, Marriage and Sexuality

SOCIAL ISOLATION

THE SOCIOLOGIST AND WRITER J. TUNSTALL, IN HIS 1966 ENGLISH study, *Old and Alone*, helped to confirm a significant observation. This was the impression among physicians in geriatric medicine that social isolation may be a trigger factor in ill-health among senior citizens. Some years previously, M. Lowenthal in the United States had pointed to a relationship between mental ill-health in old age and the presence of social isolation. We have already noted the possible effects of one form of enforced social isolation, namely that caused by compulsory retirement from the usual occupation. H. Droller in 1969 studied the various factors—medical and social—which precipitate the admission of a senior citizen to hospital care. He found that, in his randomly chosen sample, social factors —including social isolation—accounted for about eighteen per cent of the trigger mechanisms accelerating admission to hospital. On follow-up study, however, true social isolates accounted for only about six per cent of the total.

Social isolation has often been judged by the number of visitors an old person has, as well as the number of visits, in a given week. Old people who live with a daughter, son or grandchild are not considered social isolates, even though non-family visitors and visits may be rare or nonexistent.

Neither are old people who live alone but have two or more visits per week from family or friends—or both—isolated socially. Old people who have no family, through celibacy or bereavement, and no friends who visit, may still not be regarded as social isolates if they have regular 'service' visitors such as domestics or home helps, or regular professional visitors, such as home nurses or public health nurses. But even senior citizens who are living with or near members of the family may feel lonely because of strained relationships which limit real social contact, verbal communication and companionship, so there may be relative as opposed to absolute social isolation in such cases. This may be equally true where economic factors or physical ill-health restrict the mobility of the older person, who has no family and few or no real friends. Social isolation may also apparently result from a 'wish for privacy' or 'need for peace and quiet', combined with physical isolation of the old person's domicile from communal areas like shopping precincts, libraries, and community centres. This is apparent from the work of Schooler in the United States, and Ostergaard in Scandinavia, for example.

If social isolation is a predisposing factor in physical or mental ill-health—and we have already noted that ill-health itself accelerates the ageing process—then any process or activity which counters social isolation must have an anti-ageing contribution for the individual. We have seen earlier some of the anti-isolation processes which have been, and are being, undertaken. These have included pre-retirement preparation, post-retirement part-time employment, and the provision of housing which is matched to the three stations of 'effective health'. To these can be added the social services and welfare services provided by government agencies, city and town local authorities, and regional or state agencies. These vary in quantity and quality throughout Europe, the United States, and the advanced countries of Asia and Africa. Always, however, they involve activities which bring people into contact with senior citizens, perhaps through providing, on a temporary or regular basis, meals, help with daily living needs and household chores and therapy by the home nurse or public health nurse and by the medical doctor; and arranging attendance at a day centre, day club or day hospital scheme.

Further anti-isolation schemes are provided by voluntary associations and bodies in every country—such as we have mentioned in earlier chapters—and these include both general bodies of 'age concern' and specialist groups for particular physical disabilities (like hemiplegic societies) or social problems (like widows' clubs). S. Lempert, E. Goldberg and the present writer—among others—have published studies showing that the social services and welfare services are not always directed towards those 'at risk' from the effects of social isolation, or to the most needy in terms of the advanced senior citizen living alone. National census returns, government agency surveys, and local authority research can help to reveal the 'at risk' and the most needy. Studies by individual doctors in general practice, such as that of I. Williams in Lancashire, England, will also contribute to preventing social isolation and its direct and indirect effects. Williams's study of 297 patients over a one-year period showed the 'at risk' group to be in the 75 to 85 year old age group, generally in the lower social classes, frequently widowed but not necessarily living alone. He found a total of 450 types of condition which were not reported to the appropriate professional person. The reasons for non-reporting included apathy, social isolation, acceptance of 'old age' as the cause of illness, and lack of institution of proper services.

THE MARITAL STATE

The state of marriage is obviously a factor against absolute social isolation (though not necessarily against relative social isolation). The presence of a spouse means there is somebody immediately available with whom to discuss events, argue problems, compare difficulties, and share responsibilities. For the wife there is an incentive to cook a better meal, indeed to bother with cooking at all—for the husband, there is an incentive to contribute positively to the household, indeed to make any effort at all. Again, for the wife, there is the stimulus to look after the house, organise the shopping and attend to personal hygiene; and for the husband, there is the stimulus to do the shopping and also to attend to personal hygiene. For both, there is the knowledge that neither is alone in the event of emergencies, sudden ill-health, or failure of other members of the family or friends to visit as usual. These psycho-social and psycho-physical effects of any marriage are augmented by absence of a 'working role' in the husband and a 'mother role' in the wife—roles which existed in their young adult and pre-retirement years.

The total effect of marriage as an 'anti-ageing device' is thus based on more than just its function as a counter to social isolation. Marital status makes partaking of a better diet (for the senior and very senior citizen) more likely than unmarried or widowed status, in particular for the male half of the couple. This has been confirmed by A. Harris, S. Lempert, V. Cicala and others studying nutritional status in senior age groups in Europe. Marital status makes basic care more likely than in the non-marital or widowed state; such care includes suitable clothing, appropriate heating of the residence, washing and bathing and foot care, bowel regularity, mouth cum dental hygiene, and proper dosage of any prescribed medication. Marital status also makes needful medical and nursing attention more likely to be sought and obtained, so that early therapy can be instituted and hospital admission avoided. (By contrast, B. Isaacs in his most recent study of Scottish geriatric patients—called wryly 'Survival of the unfittest'—declared that the 'widowed state enhanced the likelihood of becoming a geriatric (hospital) patient'. This is even more likely if there are associated factors, like poor social circumstances.) Marital status also makes referral of the senior or very senior citizen to a psychiatric department less likely, as revealed in the study by P. Sainsbury and co-workers for the Medical Research Council's clinical psychiatry research unit in England. This appears to be particularly so among those in the over-eighties age group who have retired to a setting—coastal and warmer —away from familiar territory and people.

The state of marriage appears, therefore, to be a valuable social, physical and mental weapon against the social, physical and mental dangers of ageing. Professor L. Haranghy, in his monograph studying thirty-four Hungarian centenarians, noted that thirty-one of these had been married (though all were now widowed); only three were unmarried and these were all female centenarians. From this limited statistical group, the same conclusion may be drawn as from the Lempert–Brockington study of the over-eighties: that marital status is a factor in maintaining the life of a male senior citizen and that the unmarried state is more hazardous to men than to women.

Against the clear benefits of married status, there is the stressful point in a couple's life when the marriage 'breaks up'. The break-up may be the result of separation through the illness or death of either partner. In the former case, admission to hospital for a prolonged period may still allow visiting by the other partner so that the 'blow' is softened. In the latter case, there is no time for preparation unless there has been a preceding 'lingering' in ill-health. Such bereavement or acute separation may precipitate a depressive illness in the remaining spouse, even to the contemplation or act of suicide. Alternatively, it may accelerate a physical illness already present, or reverse a steady recovery from such an illness. Herein lies the source of 'death from a broken heart'. J. H. Wallis, a distinguished writer and an observer of marriage over three decades, has pointed out that legal separation or divorce may produce the same emotional shock, feelings of unreality, sense of guilt, and reactive depression experienced by a bereaved partner. Fortunately, marriages which have survived the rigours of young adulthood and the reappraisals of middle-age do not often end in divorce or legal separation in senior years. 'Second' marriages are more at risk in this respect, however, particularly in the upper social classes and in countries with less stringent divorce laws.

THE SECOND TIME AROUND

The loss of a wife or husband can be compensated in a variety of ways but none more specifically adequate than remarriage. W. McKain, in an American study of senior citizen marriage, has pointed out that there is, in the advanced countries, a steady increase in the remarriage rate of senior citizens. One of the factors against such a trend, McKain tells us, is the influence of public opinion. In my own study of sex in later years, *Sex and the Longer Life*, I explained some of the reasons for the bias of 'public opinion' against older marriages. These include the following notions: that marriage invariably requires sharing physically the same bed, both for sleeping and for coitus; that marriage in advanced societies presupposes physical and sexual attraction, on the part of either or both partners; that marriage necessarily requires a basis of romantic love; that marriage should always include the possibility of procreation; and that marriage should only be for physically healthy people. To these ideas may be added the objection of the children of the would-be remarrying widow or widower to their father or mother taking a new partner. How could mother love anyone else except the (late) father or vice versa? Why cannot old people be their ages? Such are the concerned questions asked openly or covertly by the 'surprised' children. By contrast, in the tribal or semi-feudal society and in rural communities, remarriage, of the older men in particular, is rarely looked at askance. This is partly due to the greater respect and higher status accorded senior citizens in less sophisticated societies. It may also be due to an extension from the medieval notion of gerocomy—rejuvenation of old men by cohabiting with young women—to the idea that regular sexual function and outlet help to slow the ageing process generally.

Most of the ideas that tend to prejudice public opinion against older marriages and remarriages have basic flaws. Remarriage may or may not be based on 'romantic love' but, in any case, youth has no prerogative in the intense pleasure and blissful delight of togetherness. It may, in fact, be easier to enjoy the companionship and attention and feeling of being wanted in a senior citizen attachment, because of the lessened narcissistic elements in either partner. The picture was put delightfully in words and music by the late Maurice Chevalier in his song (in *Gigi*), 'I'm Glad I'm Not Young Anymore'.

SEXUAL ACTIVITY

The idea that marriage should always include the possibility of procreation is a notion derived from the religious (Augustinian) view that sexual union should have conception in prime view. However, in contemporary and developed societies, the secular view of coital activity appears to prevail: namely, we consider that sexual function expresses both biological and psychological inner forces, in greater or lesser degree for both partners, and that the coital act is a source of pleasure and happiness in the mutuality of marriage. This brings us to the view that marriage invariably requires sharing the same bed —for sleep and for sexual activity. Apart from the fact that many younger married couples live contentedly using twin beds (or paired beds), the case histories in my own study of the elderly revealed a particular bias towards a double bed only for older partners in the lower social classes, whether in the seventies, eighties or nineties. Otherwise, there seemed to be no special double or twin bed 'pattern' for a given community. Clearly, factors like the continuation of sexual activity in a given marriage, or the rekindling of coital activity in a remarriage, would be likely to influence 'bed choice'. In the sexually non-functional marriage in older persons, other points like the ill-health of a partner, or the economy of warmth, or the available accommodation (if the couple live in purpose-built housing or old people's homes) can affect the practice of sharing the same bed.

As for sexuality in married and remarried couples, the reader is referred to the fuller text of my earlier book. It is worth pointing out again, however, that there is no 'fixed end-point' for sexuality in either older men or older women. The decline in interest and output of sexuality for senior citizens is very variable. It will be influenced by earlier levels of sexual tension and outlet, continued health and function of the sexual organs, the stability and maturity of the marriage and the mutual needs of the partners. The pattern will also be affected by the presence or absence of physical disabilities that prevent coitus, the degree of psychological change in either partner, and any bilateral agreement to continue or discontinue sexual relations at a given point in the marriage. Senior citizens who remarry and wish to recommence sexual relations may be reluctant to seek advice on methods, approaches, attitudes or aids, for fear of being mocked or ridiculed by the professional counsellor or physician. Thanks to the work of K. Walker, I. Ruben, W. Masters and many other sexologists, and thanks to the greater freedom of sexual expression in the general community, senior citizens who wish to go on enjoying (or recommence enjoying) sexuality need no longer be restricted either by ill-conceived public opinion, or by the projected guilt-feelings of their first-marriage off-spring.

The question as to whether remarriage should only be for

physically healthy people is open to as many replies as that which asks whether, for example, two people suffering from cerebral spastic disease or two people suffering from paraplegia should ever marry. The pros and cons are many, but the final proof will lie only in the success or failure of the marriage. There is no universal or dogmatic answer. Admittedly, the nature of ageing implies eventual decline in strength, mobility and independence—but the present writer has seen many elderly couples in their remarriages who took this 'calculated risk' and were able to enjoy sufficient good years. If other factors appear compatible—background, nationality, religious practice, personality, social status, cultural wants, for example—then the presence of incomplete physical health in one or other partner may be felt to be worth the risk.

When I gave the first edition of my earlier book the title *Sex and the Longer Life*, a number of correspondents who read it asked whether this suggested that continued sexual activity into the senior years might help to prolong the participant's life. There is no direct evidence that this is so. (The book was designed rather to explode the myth of absent sexuality in senior years, and act as a guide to continued sexual outlet and enjoyment in older people.) We did note, in the earlier chapter on occupation and ageing, the surprising longevity of a number of courtesan ladies and mistresses—surprising, in view of the risks of unhygienic contact and venereal infection. Continued sexual outlet and need into later life can be taken, in the otherwise healthy older person, as an expression of continued dynamism and forward-looking capacity. The anti-ageing effect is more psychological than physical on this count, although continued use of the sexual organs must at least fulfil the physiological principle that 'exercise maintains tone'.

E. Pfeiffer's study from Duke University in North Carolina has been mentioned several times. We noted that Pfeiffer evolved a number of criteria by which he was able to pinpoint an elite group of older people with a much greater likelihood of longevity than a control group. One of the important criteria was the particular occupational status of the men in the study so that the lower the status, the greater the chance of an early demise. In the case of the women in the study, another significant criterion proved to be the marital status of female members in each group. Where the marriages were 'broken' (due to separation, divorce or loss of spouse), the likelihood of early death was increased. Conversely, we can conclude that the intact marital state improves longevity in women. Such a result parallels the Brockington–Lempert study in its conclusion that marital status affects the longevity of male senior citizens.

It is interesting that it was also a North Carolina study, under the aegis of Duke University, that led to a significant publication by C. Nichols and G. Newman on sexual function and potency in the senior citizen age. This study showed that in the over-sixties age group, men tended to be sexually more active than women, and also that both sexes on the lower social and financial scale were sexually more active than in the well-to-do upper classes. They confirmed a survey of the present writer—quoted in his book, *Sex and the Longer Life* —which demonstrated the importance of having a spouse with whom sexual activity is still possible, as an incentive to the continuation of sexual outlet.

Specific centenarian studies from different cultures, such as that quoted in *Sex and the Longer Life*, reveal a similar pattern. In their younger years, these centenarians invariably had stable marriages which the partners regarded as 'physically and psychologically satisfactory'. Some of the couples had more children than the national average for that country. Moreover, if one partner died, the tendency to remarry was also greater than in the national average. This latter event was true even if the partner was in his or her seventies or eighties. Haranghy's group from Hungary, for example, confirms that the fertile woman has a greater chance of reaching one hundred years than her barren contemporary. Noteworthy, too, is the conclusion that loss of power by either partner to 'reproduce' does not seem to influence actual sexual activity.

CHAPTER 15

You Don't Look 75 . . . .

GRANDPARENTS ARE GETTING YOUNGER

THE DIFFERENCES BETWEEN SENIOR CITIZEN GRANDPARENTS IN the advanced societies today, and senior citizen grandparents in the same societies at the turn of the present century, are considerable. They include the role which grandparents play in today's family life, and the life form of the individual in terms of daily activities, current interests, form of speech, manner of dress and place of domicile. In the earlier age, there were relatively fewer senior citizen grandparents but, as today, grandmothers outnumbered grandfathers because of the sex difference in longevity. In former days, the grandmother was the senior mistress of a household often containing three generations under one roof. She controlled the disci pline in the kitchen and the living room, and gave advice and counsel in, among other matters, cooking, budgeting, clothing, hygiene and health. Her actions invariably supported the morality and code of behaviour of the male head of the family. The latter might be the grandfather, who was also economic and social leader of the household, or the next generation father if the grandfather was deceased. Grandparents of those days—senior citizen or middle-aged—tended to dress in a manner accepted by their own social class. In most cases, clothes were strictly functional (working wear, Sunday best wear, formal attire) and often sombre, dark and dull. The senior citizen grandmother revealed little of her femininity,

L

and even the accepted decolletage of her day was emphatically discreet. The net result was that senior citizen and middle-aged grandparents looked much older than their true ages.

The increased material income and economic solvency of today's teenagers has led, along with other factors, to a progressive focus on youth in terms of fashion, leisure, popular culture, entertainment, education, and leadership. The growth of casualness and informality, so much a part of the Stateside West Coast way of life, has spilled over and spread through the younger generations of all nations, emergent as well as developed, authoritarian as well as democratic. This informality is reflected in brightness, colour, and 'anything goes' fashions in clothes, shoes and accessories. Some of this informality and brightness of appearance has infiltrated the senior citizen's life and affected ways of speech and manner of dress. This, combined with the general availability of ready-made and mass-produced garments (at prices more economical than the formerly bespoke or handmade), and the introduction of colourful synthetics, means that today's senior citizens are brighter and more casually dressed, and generally have a younger appearance. Even very senior citizens, whose interest in clothing has been the very practical 'how much?' and 'how comfortable?' and 'is it a bargain?', are less primly and sombrely dressed today.

Clothing apart, the external appearance of a senior citizen —that which makes the observer note how 'very old' a former acquaintance now looks, or comment 'you don't look 75', depends on a variety of facial and body changes in, for example, stature, skin, hair and gait. These changes, as we have noted with reference to the ageing of internal tissues and organs, proceed at variable rates in different individuals, and also within the same body. We have also commented on some of the environmental factors which may accelerate the process: exposure to temperature extremes, dietary imbalance, physical stress and fatigue, and poor working conditions, for

example; and on the internal accelerators of age, which include hormonal deficiencies, protein and vitamin lack, and
arteriosclerosis.

STATURE

In the case of stature, there is a general impression of diminished height with advancing years. This may be more apparent
than real, because poor muscle tone and a tendency to adopt
a stooping posture are not uncommon in advanced years. The
gerontologist Dr Alex Comfort, writing in the *British Medical
Journal* in 1969, formulated a series of measurements which
may helpfully be carried out when assessing the physiological
age of a human being. Among the anthropometric tests, as he
called them, were the trunk height and the seated stature
(seated, because many persons of advanced years have some
difficulty in free standing to full height). Here, he commented,
there is a change with the years, relatively greater for women
than for men, although amounting to less than 'one standard
deviation over the interval 50-85 years'. The Hungarian study
of thirty-four centenarians undertaken by L. Haranghy and
co-workers in the early 1960s reported all the female centenarians as being of short or very short stature, and all but two
of the (fewer) male subjects as of short or short-medium
stature. Only one male centenarian was of very tall stature.
The six centenarians that the present writer has so far encountered in personal hospital practice in England have all
been women, and all of short stature. Professor W. Anderson
and N. Cowan, in their incidental studies of stature at the
Rutherglen health centre for old people begun in the early
1950s, also reported height variations in a representative
group of men and women aged 70-74. Here, expressed as a
coefficient of variation, the same pattern emerged: men 3.4,
women 4.4. O. Gsell and co-workers at the University of Basle
in Switzerland have carried out prospective studies in ageing
over a ten year period, and have reported—among other

changes—a decrease in 'body length' after the age of 30 years which may amount to 17 millimetres on average by the age of 60 years. Gsell suggests that some of this loss is due to degeneration of the spongy discs that lie between the bony vertebrae in the spinal column, as well as wear and tear in the joint cartilages.

In a very recent study, R. Stewart, H. Shepherd and co-workers in London have confirmed that there is a steady loss of bone from the vertebrae themselves as a continuing process in later life. This bone thinning, known as osteoporosis, is at least twice as common in women as in men, according to B. Nordin of Scotland. The thinning of the bone produces not only shortening of the spinal column, but a tendency for the upper part of the spine to bend forward, producing a humped or kyphotic appearance. Certain conditions increase the degree of osteoporosis, including a shortage of both protein and calcium as measured in the blood levels. The bone thinning effects are worsened by excess thyroid hormone and excess cortisone. Preventive therapy therefore involves correcting any hormone excess and ensuring adequate calcium, vitamin D and protein levels in the blood by additional dietary intake of milk or milk products. The use of protein-building (anabolic) hormones by mouth or injection may be tried. At the present time, such therapy tends only to prevent worsening of the bone thinning and relieve any associated bone discomfort. There is little significant reversal of the actual bone alteration as measured by radiography, and no increase in height. In terms of anti-ageing, we may consider the work of O. Gsell, noted above, and ask ourselves whether middle age may not be an appropriate time for general bone assessment, and reaching a decision on long term therapy with 'bone builders'.

SKIN AND HAIR

In the case of the skin, J. Hollingsworth in the United States has noted a high correlation between observable changes and the real age in years of the person observed. Skin changes were also included in A. Comfort's test battery for physiological ageing in human beings. The most familiar changes are the loss of bloom or sheen (more noticeably in women) of the skin, which generally starts around or after the menopause; the steady increase in wrinkling, around the eyes and mouth, and wrinkling and sagging of the neck and chin areas; and the increase in pigmentation in Caucasians. Less obvious, but still present, are a general reduction in sweating and opening out of the little blood vessels. The skin wrinkling is due to a general thinning of the skin layers (except the 'horny' layer) and loss of elastic tissue—neither process being directly reversible. (In the United States, P. Lindop has shown that skin is one of the tissues whose ageing can be speeded up by the effects of ionising radiation. This is an important observation, in view of the ever-increasing use of this form of radiation in industrial techniques and various branches of medicine.) Two methods have been devised to restore some of the youthfulness of skin. The cosmetic industry has given us skin creams containing sex hormones which can, at least temporarily, return some of the bloom and reduce some of the wrinkling by 'puffing out' the skin cells and stimulating production of supporting (but not elastic) underlying tissue. As an adjunct to such measures, simple lubricating creams against lack of sweating, and 'screening' creams against the drying effects of sunlight in hot climates, can be used. Less effective 'puffing out' of skin cells may be achieved by liquid or solid 'face masks' or 'mud packs'. The alternative method to creams is that devised by the cosmetic plastic surgeons. This involves surgical de-wrinkling of the neck and face, smoothing of the forehead and 'de-bagging' of the eye areas. (For the psychological and physical aspects of 'face-lifting', the reader is referred to an earlier book by the present writer: *A Change of Face and Figure.*)

In the case of the hair, there are two parallel changes with ageing that are readily observable. On the one hand, there is the progressive thinning and greying of scalp hair—on the other, the tendency to increased presence of hair on the face in women. The latter process is again a feature that is more marked after the menopause, when the oestrogen hormones from the adrenal glands encourage upper lip and chin hair growth in the female face. The growth of scalp hair is dependent on a number of factors, including hormones from the anterior pituitary gland in the skull, general body health and good nutrition, and the absence of inherited male-pattern premature baldness (genes BB). The loss of hair on the head with ageing is related to a decline in the influence of the anterior pituitary gland in both sexes, which may be aggravated by lack of thyroid hormone, shortage of proteins, and a lessened blood supply to the surviving hair root follicles. At present, there are only two possible remedies for this loss of scalp hair with ageing: either suitable wigs and toupees, or cosmetic surgery using hair implants, from the neck area, grafted on to the scalp—a technique first reported from California in the United States in the mid 1960s. The loss of hair pigment is no easier to correlate directly with a specific chronological age than scalp hair thinning and loss. Some men and women start to lose hair pigment in their third decade of life —others do not grey until their fiftieth year or later. Hair is readily re-pigmented to 'disguise' the grey effect, by dyes suitable for both men and women.

WALKING AND TALKING

To clothing, stature, skin and hair as 'age clues', we may add the balance and gait of older people. W. Fine of Liverpool, England, has pointed out in several studies that senior and very senior citizens are more often in the pedestrian state than in the driving or driven state, and that this group are at

greater risk because they move slowly, cannot accelerate out
of danger, and are unsteady for various reasons. These reasons
include being overweight for height, diminished vigour of
limb muscles, stiffening of the joints (from degenerative 'wear
and tear'), and hardening of the arteries affecting nervous
system control of muscles and joints. To these problems may
be added deteriorating vision, and increasing deafness. Further, any tendency to stoop moves the centre of gravity further
in front of the body, which encourages imbalance. The older
person may shuffle along using slow steps to compensate for
the unsteadiness, or keep the feet apart in movement, on a
'broad base'. Older persons with stiff joints may also have
difficulty rising from a low chair or sofa, and may do so with
audible creaking and 'cracking' of knee or hip joints. Many
senior citizens can compensate well for balance and gait difficulties by the use of a stout walking stick, with a rubber
ferrule at the base. Others eschew such a support just because
it is thought to be an indicator of 'old age'.

Another clue to advancing age is the voice of the individual. This is more readily noticed in singers and people in
occupations of 'excessive voice usage', such as public speakers,
entertainers, and army instructors. Any change in quality,
timbre or power is naturally worsened by excessive smoking, exposure to dust, and local inflammation derived from
catarrhal conditions around the nose and mouth. The two
main changes are a roughening and hoarseness of voice quality
(with loss of singing power in the upper register) or development of a thin, reedy, piping quality. Resonance may be
affected by changes in tongue size and by the absence of
proper dentition. The changes in quality and timbre of voice
result from 'wear and tear' in the cartilages of the larynx,
associated with reduced mobility of the laryngeal muscles.
W. Lloyd of Bristol in England has drawn attention to the
voice change in the thyroid hormone deficiency disease, myxoedema, as an important diagnostic sign of that illness. The

voice becomes hoarse and thickened in myxoedema, a condition which, as we noted in an earlier chapter, may produce a premature picture of ageing in any age group. Treatment with thyroid hormone 'rejuvenates' the voice to its normal state along with recovery of other symptoms. However, thyroid hormone does not 'rejuvenate' the voice if there is underlying true ageing change.

TEETH, SIGHT AND HEARING

G. Huszar, in a study of teeth and the mouth in very senior citizens in Hungary, has pointed out how complete absence of teeth alters the expression. There is a tendency to suck in the lips, which lose their pink or red colour. In the Huszar series of elderly persons studied, the average age of loss of the last tooth was 83 years for men and 81 years for women. In an extensive survey of dentition carried out by Professor B. Hedegard in Stockholm, Sweden, in the 60-84 age group, a similar sex difference in loss of teeth was noted, although not all those studied were completely toothless by the age of 84 years. Thus, 44 per cent of women and 39 per cent of men in the Stockholm study had lost all their teeth. The better record for retaining natural teeth is presumably a reflection of better dental attention in younger years, in particular the encouragement in dental circles of orthodontic work and conservation techniques. In the United Kingdom, as the present writer pointed out in the book *A Change of Face and Figure*, the tendency has been to extract teeth rather than conserve where possible, and to replace with artificial dentures. Strong, healthy natural teeth help maintain a youthful appearance, whereas gums with unhealthy 'stumps' or ill-fitting dentures add years to the face. In the United States, the approach is enthusiastically a 'conservation and orthodontic' one and is well reflected in the good dentition of senior citizens throughout the country.

P. Nordquist, the Swedish geriatrician, states that at seventy years, more than two-thirds of the Swedish population in that age group have no natural teeth remaining. He correlates this with a yearly consumption of chocolate and sweets amounting to 3,000 million Swedish crowns, that is equal to a weekly sweet consumption of one and a half dollars or sixty English new pence per person. Professor B. Hedegard, in his Stockholm dental study, reported that the total percentage of men and women without any of their natural teeth is a fairly static figure (around 43 per cent) through the senior citizen age range of 70 to 84 years. If we study those with some natural teeth remaining, then the average number of remaining teeth is found to be higher in the age groups 75-79 and 80-84. We may interpret this as a chance finding. Professor Hedegard has hypothesised however that 'only those individuals reach the age of 75 years and over whose biological age corresponds to (or is less than) their chronological age'. A third way of looking at this statistic is that the earlier (younger) denture wearers die off, leaving the group who have kept their own teeth to live on—a discouraging thought for the 'extract and give substitute' school of 'dental care'.

Another feature which draws attention to ageing is the change in vision that affects first the middle-aged, and then the senior citizen group. After the age of forty-five years, the lens in the eyeball loses its elasticity and can no longer change its curvature in response to calls for re-focusing by the ciliary muscles. This is revealed in an increasing difficulty in focusing and reading small print, so that the material to be read has to be held further and further away from the eyes. The effect occurs later in people who already wear spectacles for 'short sight' (myopia) and earlier in sufferers from 'long-sight' (hypermetropia). This middle-age eye change, known as presbyopia, cannot be influenced by any known therapy and is usually 'corrected' by suitable lenses. The lens goes on hardening until the mid-sixties when the 'power of accommodation' (that is, lens focusing by the human eye) is completely lost.

In senior and very senior citizens, sharpness of vision may become defective because of changes in the light-sensitive retina at the back of each eye. B. Beard of the United States, in a review of 270 centenarians in the country, reported around 60 per cent with only fair or poor vision on a self-rating assessment. In a group of 170 old people between the ages of 80 and 95 years in Lancashire, England, the present writer found a total of 3.1 per cent with disabling blindness, which is similar to the figure given by G. Gallup and E. Hill in their American study of 1960, and contrasts with Beard's figure of 5.2 per cent for the centenarian group. The loss of visual acuity includes not only changes in the retina at the back of the eye, but the development of cataract in the lens at the front of the eye. The latter can be treated by removal of the thickened lens and correction of the visual defect by suitably lensed spectacles. There is no treatment for the retinal changes, and very senior citizens have to struggle with either a thick hand lens or 'telescopic' glasses.

The change of hearing function equivalent to that of the lens in the eye is known as presbycusis. Degenerative changes in the inner ear reduce the acuteness of hearing for the decibel range of higher tones. B. Beard, in a parallel study of hearing in centenarians, found that 68 per cent had difficulty in hearing. In the group studied by the present writer, over 15 per cent had marked deafness. Many complained of difficulty in hearing the house telephone ringing, and in making out the higher-pitched voices of women. They were also disturbed by the exaggeration of loud noises—called recruitment —which occurs with degeneration of the inner ear, and makes listening to one individual in a noisy crowded room even more difficult than usual. The present writer's six centenarians all had considerable deafness (and poor vision) and none derived any real benefit from using the standard battery-powered British hearing aid instrument. (One old lady was offered a guitar-shaped plastic 'ear trumpet' and claimed it was more helpful than any electric aid.) Not all of the thirty-four centenarians in Hungary studied by L. Haranghy had marked deafness, but all had diminished hearing capacity. Some of the centenarians could hear loud noises at two or even three metres distance. The effects of occupational noise on hearing in later life have been noted and discussed in the present writer's earlier book, *Snakes and Ladders*. The otologist S. Richards, from Wales, has confidently predicted that 'modern teenagers, when they reach old age, will be considerably more deaf than their grandparents'. This conclusion is based on the exposure to excessive noise levels in discotheques, at home parties and from other pop music sources.

All medical specialists working among senior citizens agree that an older person's capacity to adjust to hearing changes is less than his or her ability to adjust to loss of vision—though both may produce, not unnaturally, a degree of depression and anxiety that is psychologically troublesome. Thanks to fashion, few people feel 'old' as a result of having to wear correcting spectacles. There is no such aesthetic or fashion-conscious approach to hearing aids, however well designed, and even when miniaturised or incorporated in spectacle frames; wearing a hearing aid is still stigmatic at all ages—and more so in senior years. Another problem is that failure to hear complete words, phrases or sentences in conversation can readily lead to misinterpretation, and begin an older person on a somewhat paranoiac pathway. Lack of communication in social or work or leisure situations can lead to frustration and a 'helpless, hopeless' attitude. If poor vision is added to the deafness, then communication by 'writing everything down' is stymied and the sufferer is unhappily cut off from normal daily life.

Some families appear to have a tendency towards earlier 'old age' hearing loss, suggesting a genetic factor in the degenerative process of the inner ear. The actual defect, which is not reversible at present, is a change in the sensitive 'hair cells' of the organ of Corti in the cochlear part of the inner ear. Apart from genetic factors, occupational noise and extraneous noise as accelerating agents in 'old age of the ear', we must again mention our old friend, lack of thyroid hormone. For myxoedema not only changes the facial appearance, as we have seen already, and affects hair growth on the scalp, but also causes deafness. Unhappily, in older persons who have myxoedema, the improvement in hearing on treatment with thyroid hormone is not as satisfactory as the improvement in other changes.

J. Fleetwood, in a film called *Living Dangerously*, presented at the 8th International Congress of Gerontology in 1969, gave dramatic expression to the hazards of daily life for older people. These hazards are increased by defective eyesight and defective hearing, so that any aids or improvements which can be brought about in these special senses have an 'anti-ageing' effect in terms of avoiding trauma which could be fatal. This is in addition to any improvement in mental health that may accrue. The contemporary physician attending a senior citizen will be on the look-out for treatable ancillary problems in the ear—such as excessive or hard wax, or middle ear fluid—and in the eye—such as the increased eyeball tension of glaucoma. Such treatment allows optimum use of the remaining capacity for hearing and seeing.

As for the other special senses in senior citizens, the ability to feel pain may become less efficient in later years. Pain sensation is a 'protective mechanism' in the human body and any decline in the reaction to a painful stimulus may act as a hazard. For example, the well-known condition of acute appendicitis produces a marked pain reaction in young sufferers—first in the middle of the abdomen and then towards the right lower abdomen. Acute appendicitis in the over-eighties may be 'overlooked' in terms of a surgical abdominal condition because there may be little pain—even though the patient is clearly ill and may be confused. The degree of change in reaction to pain varies among individuals however, and is never completely lost. Taste sensation and recognition of odours may also be less efficient in later years, though again the degree is variable.

CHAPTER 16

Intellect, Emotion—and 'Roses in December'

CREATIVITY

GEORGE BERNARD SHAW, OUTSTANDING DRAMATIST, WRITER AND wit of the nineteenth- and twentieth-century English scene, made a fascinating broadcast on his ninetieth birthday. He spoke in the thin and piping tones of a very old man but the content of his talk was that of a witty and contemporary viewer of the current social and economic British way of life. The listener was impressed by the vitality of thought, the depth of observation and the breadth of interest in the artistic and political patterns of the day. Inevitably, the younger listener was saddened by the sounds of a 'young man inside trying to break through the old man outside'. The performance of a man like Shaw in his ninth decade adds one more individual case history to the impressive total of outstanding intellectuals and creative artists who survive, still working, until very senior years. Novelists and writers still active until their eighth or ninth decade have included E. M. Forster, Leonard Woolf, A. P. Herbert, Somerset Maugham and—with recently published novels—P. G. Wodehouse and Compton Mackenzie. In the less recent past, the writer philosophers Voltaire and Goethe were active until their deaths in their early eighth decades while the scientific geniuses, Galileo, Harvey, Newton and Pavlov continued their pursuits until late in their seventh decades. Even Darwin, whose physical health was apparently never very robust, managed to continue his work until his seventy-fourth year. In the musical field, we have Haydn and Saint-Saëns, Schoenberg and Rossini as examples of composers working into their late seventies or early eighties, and conductors like Toscanini, Beecham and Stokowski working on into their eighties. In painting and sculpture, octogenarians and nonagenarians like Picasso, Degas, Monet and Michelangelo are further examples of the elderly active and creative.

Writing in the bulletin of the New York Academy of Sciences in 1965, R. McFarland advised that old age is not defined on chronology in years but, in the individual, according to intellectual and sensory functions. On this basis, the outstanding continued creativity of the artists and intellectuals mentioned above has apparently kept them in a mentally younger age group, even though they have shown physical age changes in appearance, mobility and body functions. This is in keeping with the 'activity theory' of ageing of the brain, in particular of the frontal lobes which contain and control the functions of intellect, emotion and memory. The basis of this theory is that lack of use of brain cells in a positive, active manner—the solving of problems, the stimulus of cultural events, the ambition for achievements, for example —leads to decline in the function of those brain cells. The cells degenerate and are replaced by glial tissue, which is non-functional: the so-called brain softening or atrophy. This 'activity theory' is very appealing in several ways. It suggests a straightforward and simple method of slowing up ageing in the individual, by direct encouragement of older people to solve problems, attend cultural activities, and aim at new achievements. It fits in with our previous discussion on the difficulties of retirement. It also dovetails neatly with the rehabilitation programmes for sick older people in geriatric hospitals, extended care facilities and special housing centres.

BRAIN CELLS AND ILLNESS

Unfortunately, an accurate and scientific correlation between healthy mental function and the presence of a 'normal' quantity of working brain cells in the frontal lobe cannot readily be made in the human being. Equally, the presence of deterioration in memory, emotion and intellect during life does not necessarily correlate with the pathological findings in the human brain post mortem. For example, in the Howell-Piggot series of forty nonagenarians, nineteen were known to have definite mental changes clinically in life. At autopsy, however, while eleven of the nineteen showed softening, wasting and other brain changes, eight of the nineteen patients had no visible brain cell loss or softening seen at naked-eye examination. This latter group points to a need to consider other factors affecting brain cell function—at cellular and biochemical level—rather than mere 'calls for use'.

An exciting example of this has been seen in the last three years in the therapy of the condition called Parkinson's disease or 'Parkinsonism', which affects the area of the brain known as the basal ganglia. The condition, first described by James Parkinson in 1817 as the 'shaking palsy', commonly appears in middle age and gradually worsens in the next two decades. The main features are stiffness or rigidity, not only of the limb muscles but also of the face, speech muscles, and neck muscles—and shaking or tremor of the arms and legs and jaw. In its full-blown form, the sufferer has poor balance and walking, difficulty with activities of daily living, speaks in whispers and unclearly, dribbles saliva, and often has a degree of depression and apathy. Studies in the late 1950s showed that healthy areas of the basal ganglia are rich in dopamine, a chemical substance which the body can convert into noradrenaline. In patients with Parkinsonism, there appears to be a shortage of dopamine in the basal ganglia, and Birkmayer and Barbeau in the early 1960s showed that sufferers from Parkinsonism improved when given dopa (the letters stand for 'dihydroxyphenylalanine') by mouth or by injection. Dopa is converted by the body into dopamine. By the end of the 1960s and beginning of the present decade, the form known as L-dopa was being given in tablets to good effect in a large percentage of sufferers from this illness. Of course, as C. Mawdsley has pointed out, we do not really know why there is a shortage of dopamine in this condition. It could even be due to a loss of functioning brain cells in the area. However, it does give the physicians a rational approach to treatment at a biochemical level.

Those patients who do least well on L-dopa are the group where Parkinsonism comes on much later in life, in the seventies and eighties. This is due to the overriding effects of hardening of the arteries in the brain generally. Arteriosclerosis affects most parts of the brain in greater or lesser degree, including the basal ganglia. As a result, in such individuals, as well as the shaking and stiffness, there may be changes in intellect, emotion and memory. This brings us back squarely to the problem discussed in the chapter 'The Arterial Puzzle' —that 'ageing' in vital organs is so often an effect of diminished blood supply (and therefore less glucose and oxygen, in the case of the brain) due to the three effects of arteriosclerosis —narrowing, loss of elasticity and hardening, and deposition of atheroma on the inner walls.

DEMENTIA AND CONFUSION

Cerebral arteriosclerosis, the hardening of the arteries in the frontal lobes of the brain, produces a variable deterioration in the function of these lobes. This deterioration is known by a number of names—chronic brain syndrome, organic dementia, senile degeneration—and is manifested either as a steady decline in the individual's concentration, memory, emotional control and integrity of personality, or as a 'cyclic' pattern of

M

decline with periods of worsening mental function and periods
of improvement. Even in the 'cyclic' pattern, however, the
general progress is an erosion of mental function. It is this
decline in mental function which is given the blanket name
of 'senility' and has all too often been equated in the past
with 'growing old'. In its minor form, sometimes called cerebral insufficiency, this series of mental changes may still allow
the sufferer to live alone with minimal support, at home. In
its severe form, when the patient is confused, has no concentration, is not aware of the time or place, and has become
emotional and even aggressive, then institutional care may
be required. In a United Kingdom study by D. Kay, E. Foster
and K. Bergmann, around five per cent of the senior citizen
population were suffering from mental change due to either
the 'cyclic' form or the steady degeneration form of brain
change. This percentage figure is slightly higher in those
advanced countries with a rising percentage of over-eighties
in their elderly population. In the Asian, African and South
American countries of the emergent or as yet underdeveloped
nations, the percentage figures for this group of patients with
'chronic brain syndrome' is—according to T. E. Lambo of
the University of Ibadan, in Nigeria—nearer the three per
cent mark.

The decline in memory for recent events, poorer recall,
poor control of emotions, and loss of concentration, initia-
tive and inhibitions, as well as the loss of learned behaviour
patterns—all such features of the chronic brain syndrome
described above represent an essentially irreversible functional change. However, the degree of functional change is
remarkably and encouragingly variable and can be affected
considerably by other factors. These include nutrition, the
vitamin state, the function of other vital organs—heart, kidneys, liver, lungs, for example—the presence of other illness
and the use of drugs, as well as the outside temperature,
stress and general social conditions. For example, in an old

person with the most minor evidence of hardening of arteries in the brain, the onset of a fever in a chest infection, or an episode of vomiting and diarrhoea from 'food poisoning', or mild concussion after being hit by a vehicle—any of these may be followed by a sudden state of confusion. The sufferer is muddled, loses orientation and fails to understand what is happening, and onlookers cannot make real contact with him or her. There may be passing hallucinations—seeing things or hearing things—and the sufferer may become agitated and even aggressive, Alternatively, the sufferer may become apathetic and withdrawn. Whatever the presentation, this form of mental change is potentially reversible. It must not be labelled as 'old age' or 'senility' or some other title that prevents active therapy being instituted. In the examples mentioned as causal, treatment would include antibiotics for the chest infection, rehydration and salt replacement in the vomiting and diarrhoea, and hospital observation after the concussion—with the addition of tranquillisers for agitation or aggression.

The contemporary physician is well aware that confusion —the clouding of consciousness that interferes with intellect, emotion and memory—is the commonest overt symptom of any form of underlying disease (medical and surgical) in older persons. Instead of assuming that 'nothing can be done' because of the citizen's advanced years, the doctor makes a proper clinical examination, obtaining a careful history from available relatives, neighbours or friends. He then decides which are the most likely causes of the confusion—in particular, which of them are life-threatening—and arranges for treatment of these—for example, surgery for a fractured hip, oxygen and penicillin for pneumonia, intravenous fluid drip for severe dehydration, vitamin B injections for the effects of alcoholism. Once the acute illness (or illnesses) come under control, then the senior citizen can be assessed more carefully in terms of true mental function. This may be found to have returned to normal, or to a pre-existing mild or moderate form of the chronic brain syndrome. Psychological medicine has made us particularly aware of the close relationship between mind and body, in that every medical or surgical illness also has a psychic component. We can see sharply the interrelationship of psyche and soma in the elderly person who, with a variety of organ and tissue changes over the years, is more vulnerable to variations in the conscious mental state.

Senior citizens may also suffer from the kinds of mental illness seen in younger age groups, which are not due to hardening of the arteries or to any ageing process. Kay and co-workers estimated that about ten per cent of senior citizens in the advanced countries may suffer from the mental conditions called 'functional' or non-organic. Such mental illnesses as anxiety neurosis, mania, depressive illness and paranoid states are included; of these, reactive or agitated forms of depression are by far the commonest.

DRUGS AND THE BRAIN

Possible approaches in the prevention and therapy of hardening of the arteries have already been examined in an earlier chapter, which concentrated on the heart and limb blood vessels. We observed that complete blockage of the blood supply, by clot or haemorrhage in or from the blood vessels, produces death of vital tissues in the heart or lungs or limbs. Similarly, clot or haemorrhage in the blood vessels of the brain can lead to death of vital brain tissue, in the areas of the brain controlling movement, feeling and expression; this accounts for weakness or paralysis of limbs, speech difficulties and loss of balance. In the less acute process of narrowing of the arteries in arteriosclerosis, we have mentioned the effects in terms of the chronic brain syndrome: decline in intellectual abilities, poor control of emotions and loss of memory for recent events, as well as poor recall: the so-called 'ageing brain' picture.

The narrowed arteries, with loss of elasticity in the walls, reduce the blood flow to various areas of the brain—in particular to the frontal lobes, in the chronic brain syndrome. Lack of blood supply in turn leads to lack of oxygen supply. The German workers Hackstock and Bielinski, in 1961, showed that arteriosclerosis also reduces the ability of glucose (the main nourishing substance for brain cells) to pass from the bloodstream into the brain cells. As a result, cell function is disturbed even further, and degeneration (of function and physical state) is accelerated. Various treatments have been put forward as therapy to improve the brain function in the presence of cerebral arteriosclerosis. We mentioned in Chapter 3 the use of the anti-lipofuscin agent, meclofenoxate, which is alleged to reverse the effects of ageing in terms of improved concentration and memory, relief of apathy, better control of the emotional state, and improvements in speed of reaction and in quickness of response. In animal experiments, the brain cells are stimulated—in terms of chemical processes and energy activity—by meclofenoxate, and this occurs even in the presence of an oxygen shortage. Such an oxygen shortage is, of course, present in arteriosclerosis and so the drug can be used on a rational basis. The makers of the drug claim that up to eighty per cent of patients with the symptoms of chronic brain syndrome show improvement on treatment with meclofenoxate, which is given by mouth.

Another approach to therapy has been to try and 'expand' those arteries in the brain that can still respond, in an elastic way, to a suitable dilating stimulus. A drug early favoured for 'vasodilatation', as the process is called, was one of the vitamin B group of substances. Known as nicotinic acid, this was found to cause dilatation of arteries generally, and of the brain arteries in particular. Another chemical substance called aminophylline, derived from one of the methylxanthines, was also found to stimulate mild dilatation of all arteries, including the brain vessels. In 1963, the present writer published a study of a vasodilator drug, cosaldon, which combined nicotinic acid with dimethyl xanthine. This had already been used in Germany for the treatment of cerebral arteriosclerosis, following the work of Quadbeck. (The latter had suggested that the improvement with vasodilator drugs, in an irreversible pathology like cerebral arteriosclerosis, was the result of an increased passage of glucose from blood through to brain cells, due to an increase in permeability of the blood vessel.) The study was undertaken on a group of elderly patients undergoing treatment for various conditions at a London hospital. The age range was from 58 years to 94 years and both sexes were included. All patients had the classical symptoms of chronic brain syndrome, in variable degree. The effects were assessed monthly over a three-month period. At the end of this three-month trial of the combination drug, forty per cent of those treated showed improvement in at least one major symptom. Some showed relief of two or three symptoms and two of those treated showed remarkable improvement, sufficient to allow for their discharge to the semi-independent life of an old people's home.

Since then, other forms of vasodilator substances, such as the cyclandelates, and leptazol combined with nicotinic acid, have been tried therapeutically in arteriosclerosis of the brain arteries. The scientifically based, double-blind crossover technique of studying the effects of these drugs—undertaken by the physicians in geriatric medicine W. F. Rogers and R. G. Miller, showed no conclusive benefit to the 'incurable patient with advanced cerebral arteriosclerosis'. This is very disappointing in terms of the current care of such patients. The results do not tell us, however, whether such drugs might have some anti-ageing preventive value, if given in the fifties and sixties to 'at risk' patients. Such patients include those with a family history of 'excessive' cerebral arteriosclerosis, or of high blood pressure, or suffering from sugar diabetes, obesity or high blood cholesterol.

EROSION OF FUNCTION

The extent and variability of arteriosclerosis in all senior citizens makes the assessment of true 'age changes' difficult in otherwise normal, healthy old people. In a previous book, *Snakes and Ladders* (on the medical and social aspects of modern management), the present writer pointed out that one of the 'occupational' aspects of ageing is that older employees adapt less easily to new ordinances and changed instructions. Moreover such senior workers are inclined to challenge the introduction of new procedures and recommendations by more junior staff—however expert—in an area of employment which is their own specialty. This is part of an overall lessened adaptability to 'change' which is seen in the pre- and post-retirement phases, and in both the external and domestic scenes as well. A great deal of research has been carried out by workers like D. Bromley, A. Welford, C. Eisdorfer, J. Nisbet and others on the relation between age and change (or decline) of intellectual performance and mental skills, as well as memory ratings for recent material and distant events. Their published reports extend and expand the earlier work of H. Lehman in the 1920s on age and achievement. Frequent use is made of the tests and scales of intelligence devised by D. Wechsler and modified by others. The reader is referred to the works of these researchers for details, in particular of the variable decline of some mental abilities compared with others, in relation to age: for example, the ability to retain vocabulary levels well, until extreme old age, compared with other tests of intellectual performance. Whatever the previous intelligence quotient, type of personality, skill and training, social setting, and psychological state, the general picture in the normal, healthy old person is of a gradual process of erosion of intellectual performance and memory levels. Physical ill-health and arteriosclerosis, as well as social disturbances and stress, can accelerate this decline—

so that control of these factors has a relative anti-ageing effect. The emotional state of the individual older person is related, as in younger people, to the personality traits, interpersonal relationships, social training, cultural attitudes, and daily life stresses that exist or pre-existed. To these, with senior years, are added the cumulative effects of experience, maturity, degree of adjustment, and any predisposition to, or presence of, anxiety states, neuroses, depressive states or other mental illness. As a consequence, there is no real fixed or stereotyped old person's emotional state in normal human ageing. On the other hand, we have noted that hardening of the brain arteries can produce a recurrent emotional picture—either a troublesome state, in which there is little control of laughing and crying, or an inappropriate (or exaggerated) emotional response to people, events or words. The notion that 'all old people' are 'querulous and disagreeable' or 'apathetic and gloomy' is not borne out by the studies of H. Thomae in Germany, B. Turner in the United States and W. H. Lloyd in the United Kingdom, for example.

The title of the present chapter is not meant to be fanciful. Many years ago, when the present writer had just learned to read at school, a fond uncle bought him an autograph book. Not realising that it was meant to record the signatures of notables and celebrities, he immediately embarked on a visit to a favourite neighbour, a retired senior nurse. The old nurse was asked to record her signature. She agreed but also appended an aphorism that remains the writer's favourite today. God, she wrote, gave us memories so we can have roses in December. He did not know then—she meant the December of our lives.

CHAPTER 17

Envoi: The Geriatric Scene

'SUCCESS EQUALS CURE'

NEARLY SIXTY YEARS AGO, THE AMERICAN PHYSICIAN IGNAZ
Nascher coined the term geriatrics. It is derived from the
Greek words for old and for doctor, but apparently Nascher
was describing people who were permanently and irrecover-
ably sick and disabled. Not surprisingly, to be 'geriatric' was
to be labelled a 'hopeless and helpless case' for whom no
specific treatment was available, and in whom no special
investigation was warranted. There was no age group definition, so that geriatric wards—often labelled 'chronic sick'—
in hospitals and nursing homes housed young patients with
congenital spastic disease or muscular dystrophy, as well as
middle-aged and elderly patients with strokes, severe arthritis,
dementia and other 'incurable' complaints. As O. Portsmouth
of Birmingham, England, has pointed out, the criterion for
medical success in practice has always been thought of as
'cure rate'. Logically, incurable patients with irremediable
complaints must be 'medical failures'. So, for many years in
many countries, the term 'geriatrics' was equated with medical failure, and geriatric wards were looked upon as appropriate places to deposit patients who failed to make progress in
other specialties' wards and departments.

Again not surprisingly, the geriatric (equalled chronic sick)
patient was housed in the wards of the least desirable, often
the oldest and most dilapidated part of the hospital building

N

complex—or in prefabricated annexes. The wards invariably had poor amenities, sparse decoration, and deficient ventilation, heating and lighting. (In the United Kingdom, these were not uncommonly the old Poor Law institutions and workhouses, so vividly described by Charles Dickens in his novels.) For 'protection' the ward beds had cot sides, and most of the patients were kept in bed for 'their own safety' or for 'ease of care' or because of incontinence or anti-social behaviour of some kind. The attendant staff were few, and generally unskilled, though often kind and understanding in a non-professional way. Patients stayed in the chronic sick wards for prolonged periods, confined to the four walls and limited horizon, before finally succumbing to a chest infection or to heart failure or some other fatal condition.

Meanwhile, for children, and young and adult patients, diagnostic and therapeutic advances took giant strides, particularly in the prevention of deficiency diseases and the treatment of infectious diseases by chemotherapy. The 1930s and 1940s saw a powerful medical attack on pneumonia, tuberculosis, malaria and other national killers in different countries. Anaesthesia was improved, and encouraged the further development of brain surgery, heart surgery and operations requiring prolonged narcosis. With all these medical and surgical advances, the infant mortality rate and adult morbidity rate declined sharply and—as we have discussed in the opening chapters of this book—more and more citizens have survived since then into their senior years. These patterns and elements of progress have increased life expectation at birth and improved life expectation in adulthood. The number of elderly people has therefore increased, both in absolute terms and in proportion to the rest of the population. A number of physicians, in different parts of the globe in advancing countries, and often in different regions of the same country, have been aware of both the growth of the elderly population and the need to consider a new approach to 'geriatrics', to those older people who are sick and disabled and were previously assigned the 'irremediable' label. Such pioneer physicians as Nathan Shock in Baltimore, United States, F. Verzar in Switzerland, L. Cosin and the late Marjorie Warren in England, L. Binet in France, and W. F. Anderson in Scotland, became specifically interested in the special problems, social and medical, of ageing, and in the illnesses and disabilities of senior and very senior citizens. Their interest and pioneer developments in medico-social care of the elderly led to national geriatrics and gerontological societies being formed, as we have mentioned earlier.

A GERIATRIC REVOLUTION

Contemporary geriatrics is no longer the 'passive attention and tender, loving care of chronically sick old people', but instead is a specialised branch of general (or internal) medicine and of psychiatry. Whether they call themselves geriatricians, internists, physicians with a special interest in geriatrics, or clinical gerontologists, these specialists are concerned with early, accurate and comprehensive diagnosis of illness in senior citizens. They assess the significance of physical disease, mental illness and social or socio-economic problems that contribute to individual ill-health and disability in the elderly. Older people have become aware of the therapeutic weapons available to medicine and wish to have their fair share of these. Medical and nursing treatment in its more sophisticated form in appropriate settings has been demanded by the vociferous younger members of the population, and the senior citizens are following up.

The new geriatric approach on the part of physicians, nurses and therapists is one of therapeutic optimism even in the face of apparently irremediable complaints and severe disabilities. In particular, the aim of a 'high cure rate' is replaced by a practical and realistic goal of making the older person as independent as possible, within any limitations imposed by his or her medical and social problems. This involves a basic appraisal of the nature of the diagnosis—or rather of diagnoses, since most older people have a number of medical problems, some more and some less significant in terms of immediate danger to life or to future longevity. Having assessed the medical background, the significant social and economic factors that are pressing upon the individual must also be considered in terms of relative importance. The whole process is seen in dynamic terms, and involves reappraisal, and rethinking of approach, at different points in the individual's time-scale of illness.

This pattern of approach involves linking hospital diagnosis, treatment and rehabilitation with home diagnosis, treatment and reablement. This, in turn, may be linked with local authority, municipal and regional therapy and care—in day centres, hostels, welfare and old people's communities and homes, preventive and screening clinics, health and medical centres and offices. The physician in geriatric medicine thus takes his place as part of what M. Stewart has so aptly named 'a team of people of like mind'. This team includes, at different points along the time path of illness and recovery, the following members: hospital doctor, hospital nurse, hospital physiotherapist, hospital occupational therapist, medical social worker, psychiatric social worker; and at the community end, home doctor, home nurse, public health nurse, domestic and home help, voluntary helpers (who also figure in the hospital setting), social workers. To these may be added speech therapists, dentists, physiotherapy aides, technicians and members of the clergy—and in an important role, relatives, neighbours and friends.

These members of the team 'share' responsibility for the patient's recovery in the ward setting, in the home setting, in the gymnasium, in the 'mock' kitchen, in the day hospital, in the day centre. Their presence underlines the atmosphere of therapeutic optimism, of aiming at independence and of caring that the senior citizen does not just improve but becomes as well as is practically possible.

ILL MINDS

Even where the geriatric patient does not recover sufficiently —in his physical condition, his mental state or both—or fails to respond to the 'medicine of the team', modern geriatrics does not abandon him. There is provision for a long-stay or extended care facility, or a sheltered hostel-type unit, in or near most departments of geriatric medicine. Such facilities are made comfortable and pleasant, in terms of furniture, furnishings, decor of walls and floors, lighting and heating. Such long-stay patients inevitably require substantial help with all the activities of daily living, in particular hygiene and sanitary needs. This calls for nurses and aides and voluntary workers who are prepared to cope kindly and sympathetically with patients who may be severely handicapped and have limited mental capacities. Such long-stay wards require all the equipment and amenities which are 'labour-saving' and 'time-saving' and keep unpleasant necessities of care down to the minimum. The words 'automatic' and 'plastic disposable' are keys to the approach.

Long-stay wards and 'frail, ambulant' hostels normally have extended visiting hours to allow the fullest contact with the community outside the hostel or the hospital. Relatives, friends and former neighbours are encouraged to come and see the long-stay patient and keep him up-to-date on the news and gossip. Active programmes of entertainment by groups, societies and individuals are encouraged by the professional staff. This may include visits by choirs and singers, showing films and movies, playing records or taped stories or having parties to celebrate birthdays or anniversaries of the ward or hostel residents. Diversional therapy of an elementary kind is promoted, especially if it encourages the use of limbs and joints which might otherwise stiffen up. Thus, basket making, rug making, knitting, sewing, binding and making cloths, may all be undertaken with materials supplied by voluntary groups, friends or the hospital or hostel itself. One growing form of diversional therapy for older citizens—in long-stay facilities or hostels, or even at home—is that of 'creative art'. This includes painting, drawing, flower making, and wire sculpture as well as 'indoor' gardening. All art arouses criticism and appreciation and long-stay residents can be stimulated to accord praise or disapproval, where previously the atmosphere has been one of listlessness and a tendency to apathy.

CARE IN THE COMMUNITY

In the United Kingdom in the past decade, a number of official government studies have followed upsetting reports of crowded and unsatisfactory wards, lack of basic amenities, inadequate staffing and alleged ill-treatment of mentally disturbed old people in psychiatric hospitals, and in mental homes for the aged. These official studies have revealed excesses in personal behaviour of a small number of staff towards elderly disturbed patients, it is true. More significantly, they revealed the remarkable supportive work, under frequently difficult conditions, of the majority of the nursing and medical staff. No one denies the problems inherent in the care and supervision of aggressive or restless old persons, with anti-social habits, with low levels of ability to co-operate, and with inability to make contact properly. The difficulties are greater where such behaviour is due to the irreversible changes of hardening of the arteries in the brain, which we have described in an earlier chapter. Modern psychiatry has tended to concentrate on the treatable and remediable mental conditions—the 'functional psychoses' such as depression.

mania and schizophrenia. The contemporary psychiatrist no longer feels that custodial care of the irremediable mentally ill elderly person, is his special problem on any major scale. Like geriatrics, psychiatry has increasingly pressed for community care and home treatment of all mentally ill patients. Mental hospitals of the larger custodial institution type are being 'run down' or closed, and psychiatric wards are becoming part of general hospitals. Only patients who are at risk in terms of severe mental illness are admitted to such wards, and then only for the relatively short time that drugs and physical therapy and ward psychotherapy are required to make them well enough to be 'outpatients'.

The term 'psychogeriatric' has come to be applied to the mentally ill old person who is suffering from dementia or chronic sickness needing hospital or hostel care. A. Whitehead, in his book *In the Service of Old Age*, described lucidly and pointedly the organisation of community care and day care services which may overcome the need for excessive admission of mentally ill old people to hospital. He also showed how any necessary in-patient care can be improved by team approaches, better facilities, skilled therapy and the support of family and voluntary aides, in an 'emotionally therapeutic atmosphere'. His work further underlined the value of co-operation between psychiatrist and geriatrician in this field.

In the studies of B. Isaacs and co-workers in Scotland, reported in *Scottish Health Service Studies*, 17, in 1971, two points were clearly made. Firstly, the survey showed that 'only a fraction of the total geriatric problem was known to the geriatric (hospital/community) service'. This implies that substantial numbers of ill senior citizens are looked after in the general community for long periods of time. Secondly, the rising number of very senior citizens in the community indicates an enlarging group of people with major dependency on social care and increasing need of medical services—neither of which may be sufficiently available. The lack of availability may be due to lack of funds (personal, regional, state or federal), lack of facilities, and lack of trained persons (the professional members of the 'team'). It may also arise from lack of programmes on a hospital and community basis for this group, and lack of integration of such facilities and staff as are currently available. Dr Isaacs has called this the 'challenge of the survival of the unfittest' and encourages us to face up to the situation by organising social and medical services for the elderly sick. The problems which seem to loom largest include lack of mobility, incontinence, mental disturbance and lack of hygiene—but none of these is insuperable. Solutions for tackling this kind of physical and mental frailty have been outlined and discussed in an earlier book, *Later Life*, and include laundry incontinence services, good neighbour arrangements, temporary relief in hostels, care in sheltered settings, controlled medication, nursing support and periodic admission to hospital or extended care facilities. The Isaacs study findings are not unique to Scotland, or indeed to the United Kingdom, but are comparable with findings in all developed countries. Even in the emerging countries, changing social and economic patterns plus the improved survival into senior years have begun to create an 'early phase' of the 'unfittest problem'.

We have seen, in earlier chapters, the various approaches that have been made and are being made to help man achieve his optimum life span. Modern geriatric medicine does not prolong the natural life span. It does aim to restore independence to the ill senior citizen, and, by so doing, to restore the dignity, spirit and promise of senior years—and remove the pejorative sense of geriatric as an adjective. To paraphrase Nachman Syrkin, a senior citizen is just as sacred as the nation.

Selected Sources and Bibliography

Abbo, F. E., 'Obesity and Ageing of the Human Adrenal Cortex', *Gerontologia Clinica*, 8 no 6 (1969), 370-6

American Heart Association, *Circulation*, 42 (1970), A-55

Anderson, W. F. and Cowan, N., 'Work and Retirement', *The Lancet* (Dec, 1956), 1344-7

Bennet, G., 'Bristol Floods 1968, Controlled Survey of Effects on Health of Local Community Disaster', *British Medical Journal* 3 (1970), 454-8

Brown, R. G. *et al*, 'Environmental Influences Affecting Arterial Pressure in Males in Their 70s', *Canadian Journal of Biochemistry and Physiology*, 35 (1957), 899-911

Burnet, F. M., *The Clonal Selection Theory of Acquired Immunity*, 1959

Cartlidge, N. *et al*, 'Pituitary Function in the Elderly', *Gerontologia Clinica*, 12 no 2 (1970), 65

Chebotarev, D. F., 'Longevity and Ageing Processes', *Proceedings of 8th International Congress of Gerontology*, 1 (1969), 382-5

Comfort, A., *The Process of Ageing*, 1965

Comstock, G., 'Hard and Soft Water and Myocardial Infarction', *American Journal of Epidemiology*, 94 (1971), 1

Dewar, H. A. and Oliver, M. F., 'Secondary Prevention Trials Using Clofibrate', *British Medical Journal*, 4 (1971), 784-6

Felstein, I., *Later Life: Geriatrics Today and Tomorrow*, Baltimore, Maryland, USA, 1969

Felstein, I., *Sex and the Longer Life*, 1970

Flourens, M., *On the Duration of Human Life*, France, 1855

Franks, A. (ed), *Principles and Practice of Dental Care for Patients with Chronic Disease and Disability*, 3, University of Birmingham, 1970

Grouped Flatlets for Old People, A Sociological Study, Her Majesty's Stationery Office, 1968

Hallberg, L. and Hogdahl, A., 'Anaemia and Old Age in Women in Goteborg', *Gerontologia Clinica,* 13 (1971), 31

Haranghy, L., *Gerontological Studies of Hungarian Centenarians,* Akademiai Kaido, Budapest, 1965

Harris, A. I., *Social Welfare for the Elderly,* 2, Her Majesty's Stationery Office, 1968

Harwood, E., 'Normal Anxiety Levels in Elderly People', *Proceedings of 5th Annual Conference of Australian Association of Gerontology,* 1969, 15

Hedegard, B., *Dental Disease in the Aged in Sweden,* personal communication, 1972

Katsunuma, H. *et al,* 'Anaemia and the Aged', *Report to Clinical Medicine Section, 8th International Congress of Gerontology,* 1969

Kay, D. *et al, Report to World Psychiatric Association Symposium,* 1965

Kira, A., 'The Bathroom: Criteria for Design', *Research Report No 7, Cornell University,* New York, 1966

Lempert, S., *Report on the Survey of the Aged in Stockport,* Stockport County Borough Council, 1958

Martin, A. R., 'Urgent Need for a Philosophy of Leisure in an Ageing Population', *Journal of the American Geriatrics Society,* 10 no 3 (1962), 215-24

Maslow, A., *Motivation and Personality,* New York, 1964

Michael, D., 'Golden Acres study of Oestrogens in Post-menopausal Women', *Report to Plenary Session 11, 8th International Congress of Gerontology,* 1969

Newman, G. and Nichols, C., 'Sexual Activities and Attitudes in Older Persons', *Journal of the American Medical Association,* 173 (1960), 33-5

Newman, H. H. *et al, Twins: A Study of Heredity and Environment,* 1937

Nordquist, P., *Care of the Chronic Sick and Aged in Sweden,* personal communication, 1972 (to be published)

Oswald, N. C. and Fry, J., *Diseases of the Respiratory System,*

London, 1962

Packard, V., *The Waste Makers*, 1960

Pfeiffer, E., 'Short term versus Long term Survival in Old Age', *Proceedings of 8th International Congress of Gerontology*, 2 (1969), 48

Reiter, T., 'Testosterone Implantation', *Journal of the American Geriatrics Society*, 11 (1963), 540

Rose, G., *Proceedings of Royal Society of Medicine*, 62 (1969), 1183

Scott, P., 'The Population Structure of Australian Cities', *Geography Journal*, 131 (1965), 463

Stephens, I., *A Curiosity: Long Life Among British Writers Who Lived in India* (personal communication), unpublished study, 1969

Stewart, M., *My Brother's Keeper*, London and USA, 1972

Townsend, P., *The Family Life of Old People*, 1957

Tunstall, J., *Old and Alone*, 1966

Wallis, J. H., *Marriage Observed*, 1972

Whitehead, A., *In the Service of Old Age*, 1970

Wigzell, F. W., 'The Health of Nonagenarians', *Gerontologia Clinica*, 11 no 3 (1969), 137-44

Williams, E. I. *et al*, 'Sociomedical Study of Over 75s in General Practice', *British Medical Journal*, 2 (1972), 445-8

Index